THE STINGING FLY

NEW WRITERS. NEW WRITING

Issue 39 Volume Two | Winter 2018-19

'... God has specially appointed me to this city, so as though it were a large thoroughbred horse which because of its great size is inclined to be lazy and needs the stimulation of some stinging fly...'

—Plato, *The Last Days of Socrates*

The Stinging Fly
new writers, new writing

PO Box 6016, Dublin 1
info@stingingfly.org

Printed by Walsh Colour Print, County Kerry

ISBN 978-1-906539-73-3 ISSN 1393-5690

The Stinging Fly gratefully acknowledges the support of The Arts Council / An Chomhairle Ealaíon.

NEW FICTION

FEATURED POET

NEW POEMS

COMHCHEALG

ESSAYS

COVER PHOTOGRAPH

Vanessa Ifediora

The Stinging Fly was established in 1997 to publish and promote the best new Irish and international writing.

Published twice a year, we welcome submissions on a regular basis.

The next open submission window is from December 3rd 2018 to January 9th 2019.

Please read the submission guidelines on our website.

Keep in touch: sign up to our email newsletter, become a fan on Facebook, or follow us on Twitter for regular updates about our publications, workshops and events.

stingingfly.org | facebook.com/StingingFly | @stingingfly

Editorial

At what level of literature are political concerns located? One possible answer is: no level at all. 'The only obligation to which in advance we may hold a novel...' wrote Henry James in 1884, 'is that it be interesting.' The same argument no doubt can be made for the short stories, poetry, photographs and even essays we publish here. The duty of the artist may not be to win arguments or teach lessons, but simply to find out what 'works' and what doesn't, what's interesting and what's not. In one sense, these are the word-to-word, sentence-by-sentence decisions that make up the work of writing—not ideological choices, but aesthetic ones. Admittedly it can be hard to see the relationship between a well-crafted phrase in a short story and material political conditions in the real world. But literature is nonetheless produced under those conditions, and tells us something about them, intentionally or otherwise.

Maybe the politics of writing, then, are located not at the level of the sentence, but the level of the literary culture: its inclusiveness, its diversity, its overall vitality and health. We might ask: to what extent does our culture reflect the world we live in? Are we hearing a range of voices, across the boundaries of gender, race, nationality and class, or does one kind of voice, one way of speaking, tend to dominate? Is the world of publishing accessible and welcoming, or is it arcane, elitist, cliquish, off-putting? What are the pathways into 'the literary scene,' and to whom are they actually available?

As ever, *The Stinging Fly* is proud to publish some of the leading figures in Irish letters—including, in this issue, Pulitzer Prize-winning poet Paul Muldoon, our own former contributing editor Sean O'Reilly, and former Ireland Professor of Poetry Harry Clifton. We're equally proud of our open submissions policy: we accept stories and poems from anyone, anywhere in the world, during our twice-yearly submission windows. Conscious that this alone is not always enough to reach out to emerging voices, we put out an additional submissions call in March of this year for writers who had never been published in print before. Two of the stories in this issue—Saba Sams' beautiful, compressed, fleeting story 'Overnight,' and Katie Burnip's majestic 'The Blue Slip Sway'—came through that window. Many other writers are also published in this issue for the first time, among them Katarína Novotná; Aoife Comey; and Jem Day Calder, whose astonishing story 'Distraction from Sadness is Not the Same Thing as Happiness' begins overleaf. The work of making our process more accessible is never complete, but we can keep making starts in the right direction, and keep discovering surprising and powerful new writing in the process.

For my own part, I tend to think political concerns do go all the way down to the level of the sentence—to the level of aesthetic decision-making. As far-right extremism develops its many and varied political formations across the globe, it also develops aesthetic signifiers: not only the gold-plated vulgarity of capitalist excess, but the more insidious and compelling aesthetic of nostalgia; of making a country 'great again,' or 'taking back' its sovereignty; of 'tradition,' often meaning little more than rigid hierarchy and cruelty to the vulnerable. As the art critic and philosopher Ernst Fischer wrote: 'it is the ruling classes with their political and ideological machinery that cling to the traditional forms and... invest them with the character of something eternal, immutable, and final.'

Maybe in some small way writers and artists can resist the power of this nostalgic conservatism by developing new aesthetic forms—fresh and inventive images of the world we live in, alternative ways of understanding one another. Against the repressive force of nostalgia, could we imagine aesthetics of solidarity, of variousness, of openness to experiment? I hope that the work in this volume—like James Wilkes' radical, unsettling story 'The Cultivators'; Oisín Fagan's 'Triangle'; Esther Vincent Xueming's poem 'we have forgotten'—might give grounds for hope. As Fischer wrote: 'art must show the world as changeable. And help to change it.' What, after all, could be more interesting than that?

Sally Rooney
Dublin, November 2018

Distraction from Sadness Is Not the Same Thing as Happiness

Jem Day Calder

The algorithm took into consideration the common interests, venning friendships, and left-to-right swipe-ratio-categorised attractiveness brackets of the two users before providing each with the other's profile card for approval.

At 19:15 BST, which by now the algorithm had determined as her peak time of app usage, the female user sat in one of the give-up seats at the front of a single-deck city bus where, via the interface of her smartphone's algorithm-based dating app, she encountered the male user's profile card for the first time.

Upon seeing his profile card (which, like the rigidly customisable profile cards of the algorithm-based dating app's other non-premium users, consisted starkly of a forename- and age-bearing header, a scrollable gallery of six 500-x-500px square images and, below that, a geographical location marker and maximum five lines of introductory sans-serif text), the female user close-to-instantly registered that the male user was the exact type of guy that she (and the algorithm both) would classify as 'her type'.

The algorithm took note of the haste with which the female user scrolled through, and then back a second time through, the pictures of the male user, the celerity with which she accordingly swiped right on his profile card constituting, by a comfortable margin, a record decision-making time for a user otherwise grouped into the algorithm's upper-eightieth percentile for choosiness.

After presenting to the female user a rendering of the word 'LIKE' stamped diagonally across the male user's forehead, the algorithm dissolved the male user's profile card from the dating app's main display and generated a fullscreen dynamic ad intended to appeal directly to the female user by implementing the use of her habitual search interest record so as to promote to her a product relevant to her known wants and spending behaviours. In the case of the female user specifically, said product was a cosmetic cream manufactured to tighten loose or flabby skin below the mandible.

Midway through the ad's eighteen-second playtime, the female user clicked her smartphone locked and stared out of the nearest bus window. Whether or not she absently ran the backs of her fingers over the soft underside of her chin as she watched the passing world and considered her place in it, the algorithm could not say.

The male user, supine, abed, and whose average peak time of app usage occurred some six hours later than that of the female user, came across her profile card mid-deck, roughly thirty profile cards deep into his late-night swiping binge. The algorithm arranged these encounters strategically, needling a user's most statistically likely matches into the dense haystacks of their least statistically likely matches in order to prolong the stretches of unbroken, habit-forming in-app time spent by its users.

As the male user observed the female user's profile, so too did the algorithm observe him; surveilled the way he, predictably, paused longest on her profile's lone bikini pic while cycling through the cloud-stored images retrieved from the dating app's central image database whose actual physical servers were located 4,000+ transatlantic miles from the male and female users' city of mutual residence. The male user concentrated long enough on the image of the female user to begin feeling confined by it.

In full knowledge of the enterprise's probable futility but without anything else to do before he slept, the male user conducted a few cursory social media and professional networking site searches of the female user's first name followed by select speechmarked keywords relating to her profession and alma mater extracted from her bio, the only available clues as to her identity, none of which yielded any relevant results.

More as a rendition of a sequence of ingrained, repetitive gestures than the fruition of any conscious decision-making process, the male user thumbed back to the algorithm-based dating app's main interface and swiped right on the female user's profile.

The swipe prompted the cursive-style words 'It's A Match!' to descend to the centre of the display of the male user's smartphone while, simultaneously, two circles, each containing one of the two users' main profile images, rolled to a halt midscreen beneath the bannered text—which combination of words and images always, without fail, prompted the male user to involuntarily hear the *Looney Tunes* 'That's All Folks!' closing theme reverberating from some backroom inside his own head.

Upon receipt of the gut-situated upsurge of jackpot-style gratification that attaining a new match still provided him, the male user rearranged himself on his single-extra sized mattress. Hoping to use the satiated feeling of having reached a desired outcome with little-to-no real effort as a kind of emotional forcefield through which to brave territories ordinarily too painful for him to venture, the male user circled back through his most recently used apps to his smartphone's web browser and revisited one of the social media sites on which he'd attempted to identify the female user moments earlier.

The male user proceeded to type the full name of his most recent long-term sexual partner into the social media site's top-level search bar and, finding her there, monitored the activity displayed on her personal feed. He scanned through a few new photos in which she looked like she'd noticeably put on weight, combed through the names of profiles she'd recently interacted with, read a fundraising page for a child's specialist medical treatment bills she'd shared.

Still revolving the idea of his most recent long-term sexual partner in his head, the male user navigated to his go-to pornography site and masturbated for four minutes while watching a pornographic video on mute. He masturbated neither to the pornography itself nor to the thoughts of his most recent long-term sexual partner, but instead to an imagined, holographic-seeming emulsion of the two separate stimuli: his most recent long-term sexual partner's face overlaying the porn actress' body, then the porn actress' face overlaying his most recent long-term sexual partner's body. It felt relaxing and automatic to do this.

Afterward, he speculated about how depressing he must look to the walls, to God, to the algorithm, to any of his deceased family members if they were watching him the way he imagined them, crystal-ball-style from the bright white halls of the afterlife.

Although the algorithm knew how the male user frittered his time, it was incapable of passing judgment on him. It reassured the male user to remind himself that none of this software had any vested interest in him personally, and basically only existed to furnish him with ads.

Next morning, within a minute of her smartphone's birdlike alarm sounding from beneath her pillow, the female user opened the algorithm-based dating app to be greeted with the same congratulatory match notification that the male user had received seven hours earlier.

After viewing the 'It's A Match!' animation, the female user (again at a pace at substantial variance from her usual browsing speed) returned to the male user's profile card now situated in her new matches chatlist and carouselled once more through the six images he'd uploaded to the app. She had a good feeling, felt the arc of her life bending, however forcedly, into alignment with the life of a perfect stranger.

Later that day, on his lunch hour which was really only ever a half-hour because he wanted to be taken more seriously around the office, the male user thumbprinted his smartphone unlocked and opened the algorithm-based dating app with the barely-registered intention of beginning an interaction with the female user.

With the bulk reserves of his attention allocated toward other things, the male user absently copy-and-pasted, from a previous conversation with a different female user in his new matches chatlist, the same opening line he'd used on almost every other one of his algorithm-based dating app matches so far into the vacant textbox that appeared directly below the latest female user's forename and main profile image.

Having waited a requisite number of hours after receiving the male user's message so as to appear sufficiently busy and not desperately alone, the female user pieced together a response to the male user that sounded both playful and hedging.

In the break-out area of her co-working space, she mouthed the message aloud to herself as she ticked it out on her smartphone's touchscreen keyboard, her face sunbatherly in the absence of conveyed emotion.

The female user enjoyed the clean, asensual experience of using the algorithm-based dating app, the position of freedom and control, of distance, afforded to her by its streamlined simulation of encounter and romance. She liked that it was low-risk, easy to weed out the creeps and easy to unmatch from those who later revealed themselves to be creeps; liked that its shielding, one-way-mirror mechanism meant she never had to commit the harm of rejecting anyone to their face, nor suffer the indignity of ever being rejected directly to hers.

Naturally, when it came to venturing beyond the protections of the virtual world, it was easy for the female user to foresee her own violent death at the hands of one of her matches. Even with the safeguards of being able to snoop on and correspond indefinitely with a male user before consenting to meet him, every one of the female user's eight app-arranged dates so far had prompted her to ideate, for days in advance, over being brutally beaten, raped, or (as per her foremost current concern) acid-attacked by a potential suitor.

The female user had a colleague who, before meeting any male user from the algorithm-based dating app IRL, would demand that they disclose their surname so that she could subject them to a more rigorous screening process—which precaution the female user felt her colleague, who looked at her worst about equally as attractive as the female user ever did at her best, was somehow more entitled to take.

In the week that followed, the two users exchanged thirty-five total messages spanning the standard big three Wikipedia entry subhead topics of early life, career, and personal life. Finding their outward-facing personalities to be suitably compatible, the users traded numbers and arranged to meet at a bar in an only recently gentrified area of the city within a quarter-mile of equidistance to their two places of work.

Both users had patronised the venue in the past, but for reasons not entirely clear to her, the female user pretended to the male user, both in their messages arranging the in-person encounter and for the full duration of the in-person encounter itself, that she had never previously attended the bar.

The female user disappointed herself when she did things like this, which was often. Lying ran directly counter to her moral ideal of how a person should act in the world. In fact, when judging others, the female user counted honesty as her most high-priority virtue.

She couldn't say with any accuracy when she'd become such a fluent liar. Her lies were never thought out, the same way that nothing she said ever really was, which was probably the reason why she generally preferred to communicate via text than speech, a calculative solution to the comparatively freehand and chaotic risks of person-to-person interaction. A means of revising the kind of person she was.

The anticipation of enjoyment is a feeling texturally similar to dread. Their date loomed over the female user's week like a deadline.

Walking to the agreed venue, the female user worried that she might struggle to generate conversation in the evening ahead. She reiterated several times to herself her overall strategy for the date, which was to present to the male user an exaggeratedly carefree, pretty, lite-version of her real self; a person-shaped suite of attractive gestures and responses whose outline she could gradually, somewhere down the line, restock with elements of the personality she actually had.

She discovered the male user seated on the lid of a yellow container of grit salt outside the bar. He was clad in generic menswear and engrossed by something on his smartphone's screen.

'Hi,' the female user said, earphones popping from her ears as she wound their connecting Y-cord around her smartphone.

The male user looked up from the device in his palm and, recalibrating after the transition from virtual to physical space, parsed the specifics of the female user's face; the way her bobbed hair, lighter and shorter than in any of her pictures, fell in two khaki-coloured wings on either side of her chin. She bore a resemblance to someone the male user had seen before but couldn't place, perhaps from real life or a film or pornography, perhaps just from the pictures on her profile.

'How's it going,' the male user said, standing. At full height he was, pleasingly, three-ish inches taller than the female user had anticipated.

'Good, I'm sorry I'm late,' the female user said, her voice lower than the male user had imagined it, as if concealing a yawn. 'I got the bus but there was a thing with this guy on it and we got held up. Should we—,' the female user gestured 'go inside' in a way that made her hands feel lonesome.

The two users entered the bar, the female user conscious not to over- or under-act the vacant-but-interested facial cast of a person taking in an interior entirely new to them. A popular song that featured prominently in the advertising campaign for a model of car aimed toward the millennial market was streaming over the bar's soundsystem. The male user's embarrassment at this was noticeable and off-putting to the female user.

'It's pretty busy in here,' the female user said, raising her voice clear of the music. 'Is it always this busy?'

'It's definitely gotten more popular,' the male user said, grimacing. 'But we can go outside. There's this kinda beer garden thing.'

'OK. Yeah, OK. You can see if there's space and I'll wait at the, uh—'

'Yeah,' the male user said. 'Or actually, how about you go get a space and I'll get us both drinks. It's just through there, there's these double doors. What do you normally have?'

'Sure?'

'Yeah.'

'Well, for now I'll just have what you're having.'

'OK,' the male user said. 'A Guinness with a raw egg in it.'

'My usual.' The female user heel-pivoted in a way she'd rehearsed and headed through to the outside area.

It was warm out; the summer, only recently concluded, had left in its wake a two-week coda of placid heat like a parting gift. The female user sat at the empty side of a long, half-busy table, the populated end of which accommodated a group of anthropometrically near-perfect, glossy-looking girls whose presence made the female user feel medium-sized and matte-finished by comparison.

A memory bobbed to the surface of the female user's thoughts: a former algorithm-based dating app match telling her that she was 'homely', which he had intended, he later tried to explain, as a compliment.

After the female user had taken the opportunity to feel bad about her weight and arrange her body in a way that she hoped would appear both attractive and relaxed, the male user came out of the bar with a glass of beer in each hand. He looked limited and pathetic carrying the two drinks and shimmying his way toward her, so much so that she pretended not to have seen him until he set their glasses on the table.

'This does not look like my usual.'

'I asked. They were all out of eggs.'

'I'm never coming here again. Thank you.'

There was a comfortable, anticipatory silence as the two users took sips of their beer which was warm and sepia-coloured and had an aftertaste of medicine. Then the silence lasted too long and became uncomfortable.

'So, how was your day?'

'It was good,' the female user said. '*Fun,*' she added, the word italicised by her tone.

'That's good,' the male user said. 'Most people I know hate their jobs.'

'Do you hate your job?'

'I try not to hate stuff if I can avoid it.'

'That's *brave,*' the female user said, doing the thing with her voice again.

'I don't consider it all that brave,' the male user said.

A gale of laughter sounded from the far end of the table. The attractive girls were huddled together, looking at something on one of their smartphones. The female user considered that she could be laughing more to put the male user at ease. The two users sipped their drinks.

'Do you smoke?' the female user said.

'Uh, I mean, not in any sustained way.'

'*Not in any sustained way,*' she repeated.

The male user courtesy-laughed at this but felt wounded by the female user's impression of him. He was finding it difficult to gauge her feelings toward him generally, or to know if she even experienced having feelings the same way he did. 'What I mean is, I smoked like all the way through school and then for a couple of years after that, but then it started making me anxious. When I'd go to sleep I'd start thinking about all the slush in my lungs, all the sludge and the tar, and then I wouldn't be able to stop thinking about all those pictures of cadavers and babies with hare-lips on the fronts and backs of the packets. So I just had to stop. Smoking. But I mean, I'll still smoke sometimes. If I'm with people and they're smoking, I'll probably have one.'

As he spoke, the female user traced the reassuring, talismanic contours of her smartphone through her trouser pocket. 'What you mean is, you're just waiting for someone to enable you and you haven't really quit at all.'

'Exactly.'

The female user produced a pouch of tobacco and said, 'Well it sounds like you've made a very healthy choice,' and the male user laughed and said, 'Yeah, I make a lot of those.'

In a second bar which appeared not to be part of a chain but in fact was, the two users continued to drink and perform to one another the versions of themselves they hoped someday to be. The female user laughed at the male user's theory about how he could prevent getting a hangover by sticking to one brand of beer the whole night and the male user laughed at the anecdotes the female user had plagiarised from friends.

The female user spilled nervous talk over any threat of silence and several times had the feeling of having overshared. At one point she quoted out-loud a motivational post about happiness and its relation to distraction that she had read on an image-sharing social media site earlier that day. The way the male user raised his eyebrows and nodded after she'd said it made the female user feel unembarrassed and understood.

By the time they reached a third bar, the male user had become drunk enough to have, several times, completely lost the thread of their conversation; the female user had to close one eye to keep from seeing double.

The female user liked the male user, she had decided, and waited for him to put the moves on her. At several points his hand or leg brushed hers. As they walked close together in the dense night heat the outsides of their arms touched.

Just when the female user had become fully certain that the male user wasn't going to make any kind of a physical advance toward her, he did. His lips tasted of leading-brand lip balm. After the female user boarded her bus home, the male user summoned a taxi from his smartphone. In bed, he considered texting the female user something like, 'Did you get home safely?' He decided against this.

*

On their second date, the two users spent six minutes engaged in eye contact; consumed five rounds of drinks; encountered more than three-hundred ambient, native, and overt advertisements combined; were proximal to fourteen persons suffering chronic pain, eleven Christs in statuary.

At some point the male user asked the female user if she thought there was a life after death. He looked scared talking about it, and the female user wondered momentarily if he was terminally ill. She imagined sitting at the male user's beside as he underwent chemotherapy, then imagined speaking at his funeral, his head lunar bald, visible from an open casket.

It was hard for her to say exactly why she liked the male user so much. He was goodlooking, but there was something else, a single-facetedness and fixed sense of himself that the female user found magnetic. As if everything he did was joined-up. His gait, his way of talking, his mannerisms. All connected.

'I don't think I believe in a life after death,' the female user said. Some people just smell like home.

'I'm changing my answer. I think maybe I do believe in life after death.'

'really? this is huge. what prompted this?'

'We'll thinking about dying mainly.' Moments later, she added: '*well.'

'haha. I hope there is an afterlife. I think about dying almost all the time.'

'Sounds deep.'

'I am deep.' Later, when she was watching her shows, he followed up with: 'do you have weekend plans?'

'How old are you again?' she said after.

'I think you'll find it says on my profile.'

'Twenty-six?'

'Twenty-seven.'

'An old man practically.'

'I know. I feel like an old man. I feel like I'm at the age where my life should start, like, solidifying into its permanent shape.'

'I think you'll feel like that at every age. But I'm twenty-five for a whole nother two months so what do I know.'

'That's a big one.'

'What?'

'What.'

'What's a big one?'

'Turning twenty-six. It was a big deal for me. I think I really freaked out when I turned twenty-six. A gateway year. Things start to get serious from there.'

'I think I'll save my worrying for when I turn twenty-seven.'

'Why? Because it's the age where your life should start solidifying into its permanent shape? Or because of the thing? The club.'

'The club. I don't think life has a shape.'

'Kurt Cobain. Jimi Hendrix.'

'Amy Winehouse.'

'New Star Trek guy.'

'Janis Joplin,' the female user shifted her legs slightly under the covers. 'All yours are men, by the way.'

'Brian Wilson.'

'Brian Wilson is alive, I've seen him play The Beach Boys. And also he's another man.'

'I know, I meant the other Brian. Brian someone else. It's the last age where you can still die young. And I think all my examples are men mainly because the culture has, like, an innate bias that way. Not because I'm, me specifically, being sexist about it.'

The female user nodded, which, realising the male user couldn't see this, she verbalised as: 'Sure.' In the swimming dark of the room, she couldn't remember what the male user actually looked like, only the images from his profile. 'You're wrong, but sure.'

'How am I wrong?' The male user rolled onto his side so their voices faced.

'Because that's not how that kind of a thing works.'

'Well OK then. I'm sure I can name another woman who died when she was twenty-seven if you really want me to.'

'No, that isn't the point,' the female user said, resting an arm heavily over the male user's shoulder. He was sure he could hear the smile in her voice.

Nights, the female user filmed herself. Her routine was to set her laptop on a stack of pillows on the bed and tilt its screen to the point at which she was most visible to its camera. She would then launch the laptop's photo-capturing software, begin recording a video, and step several paces away from the device to mime having a conversation, or listening, or laughing— any naturalistic activity she felt she might soon perform in front of someone. She rehearsed small, choreographed movements before the laptop's lens. Knowing she was being watched, she behaved more carefully.

The female user would then lay in bed and spend tens of minutes, whole halves of hours, watching replays of the recorded footage. She would watch until she felt disembodied from the body onscreen, until that body felt thinglike and virtual, seeing herself from the same angles an outside person soon might.

Watching the videos over, the female user paid close attention to each of her embarrassing human surfaces, the resting bloat of her stomach or slight listing of her posture. She made note of the things she needed to correct. She was working on herself, upgrading by increments. Basically only trying to be special.

'https://en.wikipedia.org/wiki/27_Club.'

The male user's reply rolled in an hour later. 'disproved by research! the three sweetest words in the english language.'

The female user replied twenty minutes after that. 'Hahahahaha. But how did we forget Jim Morrison?'

*

Sometimes they met outside his office and got drinks close by, other times they went to a film or a concert or an exhibition. Most times they watched shows on the female user's laptop.

The male user enjoyed their time together best when it was mediated by an object of mutual focus, when they shared in the suspension of their patterns of day-to-day thinking. It made being around one another easier to regulate, kept boredom out of the room. No pressure to act or feel a certain way.

When they spent time in each other's company raw, the male user felt ill at ease. Mornings, he felt trapped in the minutes it took the female user to leave his apartment.

The male user lay watching the ceiling with the female user three-quarters prone, head resting in the plane of his chest.

The male user cleared his throat and said, in a thin voice, 'When I was fifteen—'

The female user opened her eyes and waited for him to continue. She hadn't noticed herself falling asleep before. A minute passed in silence until she closed her eyes again. When she opened them once more, in what felt like the minute following that, soft dawn light backlit the bedroom curtains.

'Hey! How's it going? Do you maybe want to get dinner this week? We're going to try and set a record for latest barbeque of the year if the weather holds.'

The female user reread the message and deleted: 'We're going to try and set a record for latest barbeque of the year if the weather holds.' Then she deleted: 'How's it going?' Then she also deleted: 'Do you maybe want to get dinner this week?'

After substituting '!' with '?', the female user sent the message to the male user. She had never previously had to contact him in a way that felt so one-sided and inorganic. Since meeting in person, interactions between the two users had only ever taken place in the context of an ongoing exchange of moment-to-moment observations.

So as not to spend the rest of the evening actively anticipating the male user's response, the female user went to see a film alone. The film's central conceit was: what if an averagely attractive woman hit her head and gained the erroneous belief that she was above-averagely attractive. In the film's romantic subplot, the averagely attractive woman won over a man of equally average attractiveness with her newfound confidence.

Waiting for the film to be over, the female user thought in pulses about the male user, whom she worried had lately been distant, different-acting. Whereas before he had always replied to the female user's texts within thirty-to-forty minutes, he now took two-to-three hours to produce responses that were less thoughtful and less interesting than the ones he had previously taken a quarter of the time to write. Either the male user's interest in responding to her had decreased, or he was taking increasing amounts of pleasure in making her wait for his responses.

The two users hadn't made any plans for the coming Friday or subsequent weekend, the leisure times they most frequently spent together. The female user fretted that, without the steady, episodic structure of their routines holding them in place, they might decelerate out of the rhythms of each other's lives completely.

Although the female user had been careful not to allow the male user to become her sole source of life's pleasure, meeting him had undeniably renewed her own interest in herself. Her positive moods and feelings of self-worth were, she realised now, contingent upon the quality of the attentions he gave her. He was her looping thought.

The female user left the cinema feeling worse than she had entering it. When she checked her smartphone, the male user had not yet responded to her message. On the bus ride home, she wondered if he still used the algorithm-based dating app.

*

The male user began to wonder if the algorithm-based dating app had eroded his empathy. On some level, he felt sure that classifying women into bipartite categories of dateable or not based solely on their physical qualities was retrograde non-feminist activity, and that using the algorithm-based dating app encouraged (if not outright rewarded) many of the worst aspects of the male gaze as he was able to comprehend it. That some inversion of the gaze was reflected back at him, that he too was a vulnerable entrant into the same pageant of which he was also a judge, felt like it at least diminished the problem of the gaze—but diminished it by how much, exactly?

The male user had started to see women as oddly clonelike since getting heavily into the app, as if each woman with whom he matched was a continuation of the one preceding her. (The fact that, for reasons of personal taste, most of the women he matched with were broadly similar only intensified this distortion in his perspective. As if to gauge the extent of their sameness, the male user had, the previous week, taken two female users to the same bar within two days of one another, and had had there almost exactly identical interactions with them both.)

The male user considered the further flaws of the algorithm-based dating app. To experience early-stage romance easily and frequently discounts its value. By joining the algorithm-based dating app in the first place, users are, from the get-go, demonstrating the perforce failure of their romantic lives, their defectiveness, unlovability. Owing to the replicable means of their production, app-contrived relationships take on a modular structure, a design that fosters interchangeability. Relationships initiated by the algorithm-based dating app have no solid grounding in reality, no surrounding context, and as such unfold with the drifting narrative coherence of dreams.

Plus the male user worried increasingly about getting the female user pregnant, which until recently had also been his main sexual fantasy. He decided that, given the risks involved, he would probably never sleep with the female user again and then never really directly think about her at all after that. He felt like he had completed a phase. Maybe soon he would find another long-term sexual partner, maybe one with tattoos.

Increasingly, the male user had become host to the thought of a boring, monastic life he knew he would probably hate. He envisioned a long abstinence from sensorial immersion. He could read more, be the guy who reads. He like the way that sounded.

Sometimes the male user wanted to blunt every pleasure receiving nerve he had. He thought in the obvious metaphors, and pictured a cutting of strings.

In her cubicle, the female user laid her smartphone face up on the desk next to her keyboard and clicked it locked. She watched its vivid, liquid crystal display dim to a panel of solid black.

It had been a day, a night, and a morning since the female user had last messaged the male user, a message to which she had still not received any reply. In fact, outside of a text from a franchise pizza chain about an online exclusive deal on garlic-and-mozzarella bread and a text requesting birthday present ideas from her mother, the female user hadn't received any messages from anyone via any platform in three days.

Am I a loser? Have I made the right choices? Sometimes the female user felt like everything that happened inside a device, in screentime, occurred in something like the present, while everything that happened outside of one, in real time, occurred in something like the past.

The female user sent some productive work emails and scraped back her cuticles with her fingernails for the duration of time it took her thoughts to reset back around to the male user.

They had slept under the same sheet the last four consecutive weekends. If you counted her mouth, he had come inside her upwards of fifteen times. They had in-jokes and special places they liked. He had seen her in all her best clothes. They were dear to each other.

She knew, of course, if she were the male user, she would treat herself exactly the same way he treated her, with the same sense of touristic irresponsibility toward a life that seemed to end at the limits of his field of vision. In the saturated marketplace of limitless consumer romance, permanent positions were scarce and short-term contracts in abundance. The algorithm would dispense the male user a thousand other matches, each one fresh as an individually packaged spearmint. The algorithm's preferences for more and for new would shape his own.

If the male user sent her a long message tenderly explaining the reasons he didn't want to see her again the female user wouldn't read it, but that didn't mean she wouldn't like him to send one. Was he planning on just avoiding her? For the rest of his life? The more she thought about it, the angrier she got.

On her smartphone, the female user navigated back to the conversation with the male user in her messaging app where her 'Hey?' still hovered pathetically between them, sealed in the azure blue of its speech bubble vector.

'So,' she typed in the textbox beneath it and deleted. 'Why,' she typed and deleted. She glanced at the messaging app's predictive text function which she mostly only ever ignored. She moved her thumb toward one of the three words it had preselected for her based on her historical word choices.

'Yeah,' she selected. A new assortment of predictive follow-up words appeared onscreen. She hesitated, then chose: 'I'm sure it's going on a couple of days more but I'm very sure it is just what you could do I gotta get you some stuff out there I know I like you and sorry you know how much you're having fun I didn't want to have to do anything sorry actually,' return, return, return, send.

The Cultivators

James Wilkes

In the summer we moved into a privatised box. It had recessed downlights and a view of the bin shed. Events kept happening that summer: terrible events. Some were distant and some were very close. We found out too late about protests that we might have joined, that might have helped us gain a sense of agency. When we managed to sleep we were woken by inexplicable noise. They said it was a 'profound moral emergency', but it was happening too slowly. Too slowly and at the same time way too fast. We had some success with our courgettes and that felt like a bad joke. We tried to help our little one accept his emotions but he smashed his toys and repeated the worst of our exclamations, softened in his undeveloped mouth.

Our box was in the middle of many others. We had a small research grant and some redundancy pay. We were often at home or in the park. Our neighbours worked long hours in journalism and aeronautical engineering. If we ran into them in the communal areas we would discuss window boxes. We would not discuss the terrible events, and we would not discuss our desires or how they had started to form bodily growths. Our GPs palpated them and pronounced them 'ganglion cysts'. They continued to grow. We went back to our GPs who reassured us. Soon we wore our desires disguised under loose shirts, then we dragged our desires around behind us like lethargic pythons. Other people didn't seem to see our desires, or maybe they were too polite to point them out. We started to avoid the communal areas and especially the lifts.

We discovered that the door to the roof was unlocked. We would take our desires up there to exercise them. The desires liked to thrash around on their primitive legs. They had nearly worked their ways loose from us. They were always gentle with our little one. One day we took a paring knife up to the roof with us and slit our desires stem to stern. We were inspired by the YouTube video 'how to gut a rabbit'. We severed the dessicated stems which still attached them to us, turned their thin translucent skins inside out and washed the liquid from the objects stuffed inside. Some of them seemed to be agates, some rough lumps of manganese. Some of them were the equivalent of gallstones, and to these clung a smell of digestive juices and wet leaves.

We started sorting through the objects, wordlessly exclaiming as we held them to the light. Now and again we turned to comfort our little one who was trying to animate the empty skins. Then the door opened and the microbiologist came out. She was cautious and between contracts. She pulled down the waistband of her tracksuit to show us her scar. It was the smell that had alerted her. A hint of it lingered round her Fellini columns, the tall glass jars that filled her window boxes. Where we grew courgettes, she grew environments. Downstairs, she ran a finger across the gradients: aerobic, hypoxic, anaerobic. She explained the exchange cycles, how the sealed systems kept themselves going.

She helped us collect the materials our desires would thrive on. We took swabs from our buccal and anal cavities, our fingernails, our armpits. These provided an intimate and homely matrix. But our desires needed more than this, she told us. This was why they had tried to migrate. We took sweepings from under the bed and from the kitchen floor. We scraped the bottoms of our shoes, our computer keyboards, our second-hand books. We shredded pages of the diaries we had kept abroad, souvenir postcards, the newspapers that sustained our anxiety. The cellulose was necessary.

The objects fizzed like Alka-Seltzer in their jars. We sealed the lids and moved the columns, ours and hers, up to the roof where the light was better. We tended them. Some of them failed rapidly: unable to stabilise, they drained of colour. Or one desire would try to dominate, colonising and poisoning until it achieved a monoculture. We moved these, the pallid and intoxicated, to their own necropolis. We took copious notes. The columns that thrived developed wild internalities. We took more notes. We learned a lot about ourselves, our opacities.

The summer needed a thunderstorm to end. The pressure was affecting our desires badly. They were agitated and aggressively prowling. On the day of the storm we were up on the roof carrying out routine maintenance. The microbiologist was at a job interview. As the barometer dropped the columns entered a state of crisis one after another. One of us held our little one tight and the other, like a field surgeon who has to do something unspeakable with a pen lid, approached the vibrating field of jars. We hesitated. Do it, one of us cried, and the other plunged the ends of a plastic hose through the lids of two columns, pairing them. We didn't know whose desires they were at first, but as they merged all the others blew their tops. The contents flew several metres above us in an oily rainbow. Soaked and fetid, we waited for the rain.

A week later the microbiologist was still acutely nervous. She kept repeating we were 'out of book'. She had lost months of data and all her appetites. She talked about a desert rock she had seen scoured to a spindle by the sand. For us, it was the opposite. We were swamped by inclinations, needs and feelings. Today that seems an unimaginable luxury. Back then it was hellish. It was not the intimacy that was unbearable, but the loss of one small word. Before it had been possible to say 'I', to narrow the field of sensation down to one. Now the only pronoun we could use was 'we'. Dawn was always early. We lay in the half-light, conjoined and seasick, each rolling in the wash of the other's resentment, praying to sink back into dreamless sleep, hoping the other would suddenly collapse.

*

We were rescued from our mess by the secretary from Cousteau House. He approached us in the pocket park as we pushed our little one and the blank-faced microbiologist on the swings. His block faced ours across the park. Its facade sported a biplane mural and a council logo. He told us it was built in memory of a minor philanthropist, killed in a flying accident. When we attended a residents' meeting, he told us it was working-class housing designed by two architects who had thought to actually ask working-class people what they wanted. They had wanted double balconies and efficient smoke-free heating and the ability to share desires. The architects' understanding had been basic but it had given the residents a head start. The people of Cousteau House, he told us, had amassed three generations' experience of emotional commoning.

The residents had seen our columns pop and had guessed we would need help. The secretary admitted he was surprised that anyone in the luxury flats was engaged in such a project. Surprised and a bit suspicious. Still he taught us how to filter our merged desires, reconstitute the lost ones from traces caught in the gutters. Our lives gradually stabilised. You should meet the other water snails, he said. We found reasons to keep meeting, swapping glassware, stories, pump components. One damp evening in late autumn the secretary, tentative for once, showed us their desire tank. It was a single aquarium that spanned half the basement. We were overwhelmed. Innumerable desires, some great, some small, many antagonistic, had been led to equilibrium. One of us mumbled something about symbiosis. The secretary just tapped the glass. He directed our attention to a fibrous mat of algal growth that spread across the floor. Dense in the centre, its fine fringes waved in the currents. It had appeared, he said, when the council sent out the Section Eights. The block had been declared an Opportunity Zone, suspending the tenancy agreements. Cousteau House would be torn down and replaced by a new-build. This would have 16 flats for sale, 10 flats at affordable rents and 6 at social rents. These last were double what the residents currently paid. He said the problem was that social rents were pegged to private rents, and private rents were skyrocketing. He didn't say: because people like you have moved here.

We had our own problem: a type of desire we had named 'desire to live right'. Hyphal and delicate, it extended rust-coloured filaments up and down our columns with comic desperation. If things didn't change it would collapse and die, sending our environments into toxic shock. We tried every patch we could. We tweaked our sedimentation and nitrate levels, we shopped ethically, we took in parcels for our neighbours. The overextension slowed for a time and then continued faster. When the secretary proposed that we common our desires with theirs we were surprised. We asked for a few days to think it over.

We knew that the process was irreversible. No filtration system could unweave such a living tangle once it was established. Our desires would thrive or die with theirs. We started a list of the pros and cons. Two hours later one of us knocked the dregs of the wine over it. It didn't matter. The microbiologist was relocating to Lisbon, where she would have access to a lab. She hoped the change of culture would do her good. We had neither the technical background nor the resources to up sticks like her. The residents were offering us charity. They were extending a lifeline, and we would take it.

*

You probably want to know what it was like. There was no great cosmic merging. It was more like slowly taking a bandage off, or learning to separate the sounds of a new language. Life is more acute, which for now, for us, means painful. The algal mass is greedy for nutrients. It leaves our desires with little. We do what we can to control the self-destructive outbreaks that result. We tinker, we clean, we tithe our energy and skill.

You probably want to know if we're better people. We aren't. Only this: we can't shut out the cry, and so of course we give. Out of love, out of recognition, or simply to end the pain of it, we give whatever we can. To others, to ourselves. We know each other imperfectly. We misunderstand, and worse. We harm each other, sometimes not even recognising the weight we're placing on a deep and tender bruise. We get it wrong, we get it wrong. So much so that we worry that 'we' is a cover, a mask. Because our vulnerability is not evenly distributed, and this can't be undone. Still we say 'we' and in that joining of voices we make a claim on the future, and a promise to it. We: we are weary with the sense of things being done to us. Some of us have no right to be weary: we know the world has always unrolled beneath our feet, but we feel it nonetheless. Do you see? Ought has no purchase against what simply is. It's not just the battle with the council and developers, an ugly fairground ride swinging higher and higher. It's a battle with the whole assemblage that has been pressing on some of us, many of us, and so all of us, for a lifetime, for many lifetimes.

You maybe want to know what we dream of. It used to be nightmares of total collapse, paralysis by noxious bloom. We prepared a chlorine mix, ready by the tank, in case permanent anaesthesia came to seem better. That's behind us for now. We dream of small instances of justice and joy and sometimes we get to see them seeded in the world. Yesterday we found a wayward desire putting out feelers in the tank. It was a small and vulnerable yearning. It concerned a sweetened rice dish the dreamer hadn't tasted since childhood. We are doing what we can to nurture it. If it thrives we will celebrate. If it dies we will mourn.

Perhaps you want to know what keeps us going. When our little ones bud their own desires we slip these into the tank and then we throw a party. We dance together, slowly, in the community hall with all the lights on, in the darkness of an early January evening. We know we look foolish and ungainly but none of us feels it. This gives the dance, and us dancers, an easy weight. We move in various ways, in our various times, because we want to express what we share: hope for the new desires. For the ways those desires might meet the world we're able to patch together. And we continue to believe that desires can bud spontaneously, laterally. That boundaries can be thinned. Passing strangers in the street we look surreptitiously for the signs of this. Then we look more boldly.

Yoshi's Island 3

Today I climbed the highest peak in this region the Windy Mount.

My singular wish was to see what its elevation offered.

With one companion my brother who is no better or worse than

anyone else I saw blankets of mushroom fields reducible

to patchworks what the birds' eye view must see of farms in Genoa.

I went so far up the broken path I supposed I should almost

see the curve of the planet or the whim on which the waves begin

but for the first time in some time I thought of our father at home

the Sirocco in from the south turtle doves in the huge wheat fields.

Stephen Sexton

Yoshi's Island 4

Salt water everywhere low tides undulate a flotsam of mines

the archipelago aswim with joyful blue-white puffer fish

and in a neighbouring province saguaro prowl a feline prowl.

Since it's August she begins the idle effacement of dying

the many prickles of needles of many exotic compounds

hormones and corticosteroids the stiffening of the larynx

mouth the dry of the walk alone into the desert finding there

those cactuses their open arms and their long curious shadows.

Stephen Sexton

#1 Iggy's Castle

My dreams reply the garden has become an ocean of lava

a precinct of spewing tephra the rock like black honey folding

over again impossibly and yet on a shaky island

someone is standing surrounded by fire who says go without me.

So there is a sound in the house when I wake mice under the moon

my mother who cannot sleep halves a bright grapefruit whose feet whose toes

whose hands whose fingers whose ankles whose head she says are on fire.

Stephen Sexton

The preceding three poems are excerpted from Stephen Sexton's forthcoming collection *If All the World and Love Were Young*, due from Penguin in May 2019.

Employment

Aoife Comey

At midday Jacob struggles through the door with his bicycle. One leg of his jeans is rolled up and his bicycle makes a soft ticking sound as he wheels it behind the low desk at which I am sitting and props it up against the wall. I don't draw his attention to the trail of grime he has left on the floor.

It's raining heavily outside, and all morning I've allowed myself to be transfixed by translucent rivulets of rainwater streaming erratically down, and sometimes across, the long rectangular window panes. My dog is asleep on a cushion a few metres away from me. One of her long ears drapes over the edge of the cushion onto the floor; the other folds back on itself revealing the impossibly tender pink skin on the underside. She always arranges herself on her cushion in such a way that at least one part of her body touches floor.

Without taking off his helmet, Jacob sets his backpack down on the desk, unzips it and produces a fern. Its texture is diaphanous and I have a strong desire to put my hand through it, to prove to myself that it's tangible. It's such a startlingly saturated shade of green that it seems to glow.

I swung by the garden centre en route, he says. And picked up a fern. Specifically, it's an asparagus setaceus.

He reads the Latin name on the tag while cutting it off one of the fern's wiry branches, to which it had been attached like a hospital bracelet.

Apparently it's not technically a member of the fern family, he says. But it looks like one.

I think of the ferns which grow as weeds in the hedgerow at the bottom of my mother's garden—which is less a garden than a patch of wild, boggy land—and of how absurd it would seem if I dug one up and potted it.

The ferns I've seen in the wild are more cruciferous-looking, I say.

It's January and the sky is the shade of pale wintry grey against which distant trees might appear dark reddish purple, though the view from the shop window is not remotely pastoral. The segment of the opposite side of street which is visible to me consists of abandoned shop fronts in varying states of dereliction. Weeds sprout from the guttering, and tattered and discoloured net curtains hang in all of the upstairs windows. I've always found net curtains repellent. I think there's something spectral and awful about them, and the sight of them makes me feel slightly ill.

The street on which the shop is located is in the vicinity of the city's financial district and the wider neighbourhood is rapidly gentrifying. If you stand outside the shop, turn your head in any direction and look up, you'll see that cranes and modern buildings crowd the sky and that several of the street's retail units are under renovation. The extent to which the shop is complicit in the area's gentrification is something Jacob and I worry about, though, as—technically—a small, struggling business, the shop is hardly the driving force of the property market. The same thing can be said about the boutique flower and knitting shops on the street too, but this fact doesn't negate the disparity between the demographic profile of our respective customers and that of the wider neighbourhood.

Jacob usually points out that we could always go back to having real jobs like the progeny of the professional middle class are supposed to. I never address his presumption in including me in this demographic category, in part because I dislike confrontation and in part because I find it flattering. The truth is that I'm strangely drawn to the aesthetics of corporatism. I sometimes open the shop for 9am just so that I can join the financial commute and pretend to myself that it's necessary to jog up the subway elevators.

Jacob pulls out a bag of soil and a stack of second-hand terracotta pots, a gift from the owner of the garden centre. The pots are faded and stained green; some of them are chipped. Jacob sits back on his heels and absently strokes Lola behind her ears while she sniffs at the pots. He chooses the second largest pot and puts the rest back under the display table. He spreads some newspaper on the ground, holds the fern upside down over the newspaper with his left hand closed lightly around the base of the stems and gently squeezes the plastic container to release the roots. He lines the chosen terracotta pot with soil, which he scoops from the bag with a tablespoon, and places the fern inside it and packs soil around the sides. When he's finished, he puts the fern in the window display and turns to me with an amused expression.

Jacob's eyes are heavily lidded and slant slightly downwards. When he smiles they become animated in a way that seems disarmingly earnest. His facial structure is very different from mine and, by default, conveys an air of both self-command and sensitivity. Sometimes I wonder what my life would be like if I had his face. When I see photographs of myself I'm always horrified by how anxious and alarmed I look. One time in a job interview one of the interviewers said: I hope you don't mind me saying this but you look absolutely terrified. In response I apologised and said that that was just the way my face was, which made all three interviewers laugh.

Doesn't the word 'cruciferous' refer to the cabbage family? he finally asks.

I've no idea why I said that, I say. I think I meant that ferns have more substantial fronds.

Ah, possibly.

I grew up on the periphery of an agricultural community and have an embarrassing compulsion to appear authoritative in matters concerning the natural world, in order to compensate for my lack of knowledge about it. Jacob sits on the edge of the window display, shivers and takes off his cycling helmet. His clothes are wet, particularly the thighs of his jeans, and I notice that the hair which had been covered by his helmet is as wet as the strands which had been exposed to the rain, a sign that he isn't long out of the shower. His head is bowed and he silently picks his fingernails.

I should wash my hands, he says after a while, holding them out and spreading his fingers. They're absolutely filthy.

I watch him disappear up the small staircase at the back of the shop. The shop is a bookshop and Jacob is its owner, despite being only twenty-eight, two years older than me. The inside of the shop is modern and dimly lit, partly due to the positioning of the light fixtures but primarily due to the proximity of the buildings across the street. Customers regularly comment on how beautiful it is. It contains lots of indoor plants and is illuminated by reading lamps positioned at intervals along and attached at varying heights to the book shelves. Thank you, I always say, though the aesthetic of the shop has nothing to do with me.

Jacob is very selective about the books the shop sells. He likes to see himself as a discerning curator, and I suppose he is. Although, even if I had contempt for his taste and personally disliked him, I would still probably agree with everything he said. By now I consider Jacob a close personal friend, but his status as—technically—my boss is an unspoken source of tension in our relationship.

In spite of all the handsome reading lamps and indoor plants, the shop receives relatively few customers. On weekdays there are hardly any at all before the afternoon. The few who do enter are usually alone, peruse blurbs and opening pages for up to half an hour and leave without buying anything. They also usually thank me on the way out, mouthed more often than spoken. In the beginning, it used to appall and mortify me to be alone in be such close quarters with strangers. My senses would be on high alert for every step, breath and page turn. Now I find the intimacy and stealthiness of these occasions calming and strangely exhilarating, like being in the presence of a peaceful, though potentially dangerous, ruminant animal.

Weekends are much busier and bring customers of a different ilk. They're more fashionable, boisterous and urbane, and come mostly in twos and threes, overspill from the nearby street market. I prefer the weekday crowd. Sophie, an old friend of Jacob's, works in the shop on weekends. She's acerbic, has a nose piercing and is a PhD student in the English department of one of the city's most prestigious universities. She has worked in the shop since it opened almost two years ago, a lot longer than my two and a quarter months.

The first time I met Sophie was also the first time I met Jacob. She was standing on a step ladder rearranging books on a high shelf, and Jacob was sitting at the desk with his legs crossed. It was a starlit Saturday evening in November and my breath was visible in the cold air. From outside, the brightly lit interior of the shop seemed to me like a stage set, and Jacob and Sophie like louche, attractive actors in a bourgeois play.

I had lost the run of myself that week. On the Monday I quit my job (with immediate effect) as a dogsbody at a venture capital-funded internet platform and by the end of the week I had finalised Lola's adoption from a local animal shelter. I decided to adopt her more or less on a whim on the evening of the Monday that I quit my job. I came across her profile on the website of a local animal shelter, dialled the number provided underneath and called it. On her profile it said she was looking for a new home following the sudden and unexpected death of her 'human', an elderly woman called Veronica, and that the trauma of losing Veronica had left her insecure, though she was otherwise very affectionate and playful.

When I called my mother to tell her about these developments, I could almost hear her trying to decide what to say on the basis of her snap assessment of my psychological state.

Could you not have hung on until you found something else? she asked. Was it really that bad?

It's more that it was pointless and degrading, I said. Are you ashamed of me? As I asked this question it occurred to me that maybe I was ashamed of myself.

Of course I'm not ashamed of you, she said quickly. I'm just sorry you're finding it so hard to find a job that makes you happy.

I don't really have any faith in that happening, I said. I considered sneering at the idea of finding happiness in a job but decided against it. I was holding the phone between my shoulder and chin. When my mother spoke again, I analysed her voice for intonations suggestive of exasperation. She said she'd transfer some money to my account and asked tentatively if I was eating properly. Then she gently enquired as to whether Lola could be returned to the animal shelter, in response to which I asked if she would ever consider returning Dougal to the animal shelter. Dougal is my mother's pampered springer spaniel. When she walks him, he trots sedately at her heel, while gazing up at her with such devotion that strangers stop their cars to ask for training tips. The trick, she tells them, is to get a clicker. When Dougal pulls on the lead, she gives the clicker two vigorous clicks and he scrambles to her heel and sits up straight like an army cadet standing to attention, an image of man's dominion over nature.

No, I wouldn't, she said.

As she spoke, I was watching Lola who was lying on my bedroom floor. Her face was turned away from me but I could see from her shadow on the wall that her eyes were open. Apart from embarrassment and resentment at her apparent indifference towards me, I felt nothing for her beyond the mixture of guilt, despair and compassion which I feel for most living things if I think about them for long enough.

It's just that, she said, a dog is big commitment, especially when certain aspects of your life are, you know, in flux.

Obviously, I knew she was right.

That evening in front of the book shop, I picked Lola up, supporting her chest with my left arm under her front legs and supporting her back legs with the crook of my right arm. With my shoulder, I pushed at the unyielding door and momentarily caught Sophie's eye through the window.

It opens outwards, Jacob said, pushing it open. Sorry, I know it's a pain. I thanked him and he fussed over Lola, stroking her under her chin, his face about an inch from her long placid muzzle.

I love spaniels, he said. I had a springer when I was growing up. You can put her down and let her walk around if you like. We're a dog-friendly establishment. As in we like having dogs about the place.

Sophie coughed at the word 'establishment' and smiled down at me from the step ladder. She resumed rearranging the shelf. I set Lola down and detached the lead from her collar. Jacob picked up a stack of books from a cardboard box on the floor and wordlessly handed it to Sophie. I scanned the display table and picked up a book with an illustration on the cover which I could only describe as 'lurid'. I turned it over and read the entire blurb without taking in the import of a single word. If someone had asked me what I was reading, I would have said 'who knows.' I returned the book to the display table and picked up another.

I just find it makes all the difference to be able to talk about it, Jacob said quietly to Sophie. And I know it's a luxury that most people can't afford.

He was standing at the base of Sophie's ladder, fidgeting with a reading lamp.

I mean if you can afford it and you think it's helping, then why not? Sophie said absently. I know it really helped my friend after her dad died and her best friend committed suicide.

I'm probably too self-indulgent, Jacob said.

His voice was lowered almost to a whisper but I could still very clearly hear every word he said and I wondered whether he was aware of this.

Sophie didn't respond to this comment. I couldn't see either of their faces as I was facing the bookshelves on the opposite side of the shop, and had my neck bent over an open book of short stories by a long-dead female writer. No one spoke again until I approached the desk to pay for the book.

Such an underrated writer, Sophie said. She was at floor level, having descended from the ladder. That's actually my bath book of choice. You should see how tattered my copy is. I've dropped it in the bath like twice.

Since when do you bathe, Sophie? Jacob asked.

As in, wash? Sophie responded.

As in, soak.

Since I've had access to a bath that isn't too gross to use, Sophie said. So, I've always bathed, with intermittent gaps. Why?

No, I just didn't think you seemed like the kind of person who would, Jacob said, scanning the book. Actually I haven't heard of this author before. I'm constantly finding new blind spots.

Jacob never reads books by women, especially if they're about women, Sophie said. He only reads serious books about war and the human condition.

Sophie has no respect for great art, Jacob said.

I just have a healthy loathing for the white male canon. Is that so wrong?

No, but it probably means you'll never be considered 'well read' by serious people.

A prospect of inconceivable horror, Sophie said. You can be so cruel sometimes.

Although when you've finished your PhD no one will actually believe you when you say you haven't read Nineteen Eighty Four. Or the Russians.

Can I just say that it sends shivers down my spine when you refer to 'the Russians' like that? Sophie said, which made me laugh.

Don't encourage her, Jacob said, handing me the card reader. I entered my PIN and handed it back to him.

Would you like a paper bag? he asked.

Thanks, but I have a backpack, I said. And I'm trying to cut down on single-use packaging.

Aren't books made of trees? Jacob said.

They are, aren't they? I said. Although I guess they're not necessarily single-use.

I reattached Lola's lead to her collar and put my hand on the door handle. Then I said: Actually, are you hiring at all?

Potentially, Sophie said, after she and Jacob quickly exchanged glances. When could you start? If you're asking for yourself that is.

I haven't worked in a bookshop before, I said. I don't know if that's a problem.

Neither had we, Jacob said. I hadn't actually worked in a shop of any kind.

Different rules tend to apply when one controls the means of production, Sophie said.

Jacob is descending the stairs now, presumably with freshly washed hands. He looks past me through the window and says that it's stopped raining, that if he stayed in bed for an extra hour he wouldn't have got drenched on the way here.

You get no thanks for being an eejit, as my grandmother would say, he says.

I walk to the door and open it.

I, therapist

After Dr Susie Orbach

With you / I am pomegranate
lung, sweet alveoli seed bursting
at the teeth of you, the stain of me
I cannot, at any cost, let touch you.

With you / steel wool nibble gnaws
my elbow crease, ceaseless
itch at the back of my knees.
You won't tell me what. can'twhatcan'tstop.

With you / I am water, bone becomes =
blue, pure H2O hue, infinite
and giving. But it was not me that
was called here to drink.

With you / I am the dandruff
dusting these cake wedge shoulders,
I am the gawked-at in a poundland paperweight.
Thank god now snaps the clock. Day. Over.

You spear me, spite me, stroke
in me something that has banished
its own name, there are not-word
things you need me to know.

Eye have trained my I years this alchemy
  this gut to word
                        this vein to verb
this skin is always seeking a syntax.

But you / you / you / you steal
of me my sorcery, my man-made
mystery, all I can do is lick the salt
of you, bathe in your animal wound.

Eloise Stevens

Germ Dance

John Vaughan

I held my mother's face in my hands and tried not to drop it into the grey vacant lot below as I showed her the nothing view from my balcony. Can you see it? I asked, meaning: was I right to come here? The pixels of her face underwent a brief turbulence before settling again. She said: It's beautiful. I wouldn't go that far, I challenged. I juggled simultaneous conflicting desires: I wanted my mother's approval yet resented and even scorned her interference. This had significantly damaged our relationship, but sometimes it resulted in moments of miscommunication so jarring it was comical. Fine, she replied, it's hideous. It makes me want to cry. Sorry, she added, wincing. I know you don't like that word. It's *unfortunate* looking. How's that? She often apologised to me personally when she insulted someone's looks, as if I took offense on behalf of another member of my kind. It was her way of reminding me that she was beautiful and I wasn't.

In her youth my mother had been a rather successful model. She spent long, boring hours waiting around and being told to smile, look up, play sexy, play dead. In primary school, at a time when children develop, expand, and learn how to break people from the inside, boys with holes in their eyes and girls without real voices would come up to me and tell me about her. I was shown images and videos of her on the internet from when she was young and, so she told me, could melt the face off her enemies and lovers alike with a glance. One video I remember showed a close up of her eyes blinking in dread slow motion; her lashes came down like whip cracks, her expression that of a doctor's patient confused, almost indignant, about a diagnosis of impeccable health.

She never came out and said it, but the truth was that my untimely arrival had in some inalterable way ended her career. She called on old friends and contacts in the business, asking them for help, often over the phone, so that I could watch her expression barely hold itself together as the person on the other line carefully dismantled her hopes and dreams. I didn't know exactly who my father was. Every birthday, until I hit sixteen, I would ask for her to tell me who the man was. She said things like, He's a nobody, He's a loser, He broke my heart and shoved the pieces down my fucking throat. I stopped asking when she started seeing J. I had figured there would be a time when I would have to turn away from home and, for me, it was when terms like 'father' and 'safety' enjoyed equal liberation from their supposed meaning. If, for whatever cruel reason, I was led to introspection, I envisaged myself as a creature of primitive instincts, one who would wake in the middle of the night, gather my things in a neat bundle and go. I would walk into bars populated by ruined men collapsed over their drinks, and I would utter phrases like 'I left my man for the road' or 'I am a broken woman.' Of course this wasn't me and never could be. Instead I took off shortly after J moved in and enrolled myself at one of the many institutions in the city for over-educated, dreamless youths.

When I arrived I was given a choice of employment between butcher and administrator. Somehow the latter sounded more violent than the former, so I quickly became a butcher of mediocre talents. Customers would come in and point to specific cuts of meat, asking politely for me to eliminate fat, pluck out bones, or impale chunks of meat on long thin rods. I won't lie: I sometimes took pleasure in deliberately mucking their order. More than once I handed over a bag of meats to a customer and watched them leave completely unaware of the cow's heart sidling up against their chicken goujons, avuncular and invasive, bloodying the breadcrumbs. I preferred working out back in the refrigerated room, where I hacked away at the meat that hung from hooks. The process of de-familiarization was amazing to me. I wondered how my own body would look when stripped and laid bare before another. I thought it might look like a steak, and I was always amazed when it didn't. Whenever it was my turn to close up shop, I took advantage of the empty space and tapped into my animal. I turned the lights off, went out back, got down on my hands and knees and bayed remorselessly, like I was the last of my species, like I was the last living thing. I nudged the frozen limbs of shadowy carcasses, and waited for their equilibrium to swing them back and nose me gently. This was intimacy.

I paid nightly visits to my reflection. I could only withstand the sight of it in certain schemes of light; in particular, the light that puts out blue paws along the concrete and slowly bruises the window. Naked, I would stand in front of the mirror and begin the inspection. My hands, hanging by my hips, would mobilise and rove around the landscape gently cast in blue. I didn't know exactly what I was looking for. I resented the results that often came up on the internet—they were so closed-minded, so tied to logic, so lacking in imagination. Vaguely, and with no feeling, I cruised along my body, searching for a mouth where no mouth should be, a whispering hole, something, anything, at the very least a physical manifestation of what I believed to be my fatal illness, a thing upcoiled and undetected, clotted and suspended between my corset of bones. I took no pleasure in these events: the longer I looked at my body, the more it seemed to take on its own alien identity. It looked like it might slip out of view and twist into the night to tango with Francis Bacon's grimacing misfits. More than once I willed it to. I toyed with the dream of ditching my body. Then again, I toyed with a lot of dreams, only some of them my own.

I was provided with earplugs but I preferred to sleep exposed to the world. I heard alarms, car horns, the distant, diligent thud of sentient machinery. The occupant in the room next to mine frequently rubbed our shared wall, with a hand I presume, and the scuffling noise registered deep within my body. It was not unusual for me to send out a searching hand; I imagined a hand meeting mine in silent, uproarious defiance of what some experts had dubbed the Death of Contact. I knew that one day I would find myself locked out, shut in the long corridor of shame with the lights blowing out one by one, and the hand that held my hand would suddenly squeeze, crush, and drag to bubbling depths. I had no plan for when that moment came. Perhaps it will never come, I sometimes thought, the way I sometimes closed my eyes during violence in a movie or in passing a beggar shivering in the cold.

There were weekly parties thrown to universal dread. They were supposed to encourage the construction of meaningful relationships between us, but what usually happened was far from meaningful, and only technically relational. I was not a talented dancer by any stretch of the imagination, but that did not stop me from stepping onto the dance floor, closing my eyes, and swinging my arms around, disco fingers wagging to the beat. Snake-hipped girls would swoosh past me, using their bodies in ways I envied hugely, and if they caught me looking at them they would snap shut and slink away. The males mostly looked like lost pedestrians. Others had the total disregard for scrutiny and an uninhibitedness that only children and natural disasters possess. Ida—the girl whom, after a while, I had come to suspect to be my neighbour—came up to me one night and asked me would I like to dance. Looking at her, one could almost hear the sound of her body uniting in seamless harmony, the contact of bone upon bone. I am dancing, I replied. She looked put out, so I fished around for her hand and reeled her in. Try to keep up, I laughed. After a few songs, I leaned in and asked her, Do you dream at night? All the time, she said. Of the walls coming down? I asked. We had both stopped dancing. She nodded. We stood there—for how long I don't know—until the alarm rang out, the lights came on, the faces reverted to their habitual impassivity, and we were all dismissed. That night I lay awake until I heard the familiar scuffling along the wall. I could no longer tell if my eyes were shut or wide open.

She came into the butcher one day not long after our dance. Good evening, miss, I said. Why, hello there, you, she replied. I blushed mightily (what would the customers think! there were children present!) and bent my head so as not to betray the furious passion in my eyes. I watched her hands as she requested a large portion of mince. Would you be in the habit of dining alone, miss? I asked. She nodded, adding: It's a filthy habit I'm trying to kick. I did not let her hands leave my sight: like fish in water they bobbed, waiting for me to follow them. Finally, I asked: In that case, I see it as my personal duty to share that mince with you. Our eyes met. Coins, forgotten, fell and startled several customers. All the air had been sucked out of the shop.

Every few days, usually in the evening, men would break free from their rooms and you could hear them walking down the hallways, knocking on doors with one hand, peering into the keyhole and asking to be let in. They did not care which room they entered. I knew not to let them in; when J moved in with me and my mother, I had learned to lock my door at night, or, if something was to be endured, to feign sleep and transport myself to a different body, a different world. It did not occur to me that not everyone had received such thorough education. It did not occur to me that one evening, while I lay cooling off by the window, Ida would open her door and let the wrong man in. Before I knew what was what I had burst into her room and howled at the man to leave her alone. He had a goofy grin and vacant eyes. Oh, he breathed, you want to join? Ida called him ugly names as I beat his head with my bunched up fists, and I looked at her over my shoulder. We smiled and continued our onslaught; we made a good team. Eventually the man left, or else he was wheeled out. Thank you, she said. I did not make to leave. She did not ask me to. That night I dreamt of walls coming down and it was not night and I was not dreaming.

How to Leave

it's been years
since I last saw Prešov turn brown in winter
it's been countries
—loves lost
and cousins dead—
since I last saw my mother's Manchester jacket
and my father's knuckles frozen in the wait
for the windshield to thaw

times go and never come back
like cut hair clogs the drains and barks echo
in the wet corridors paved
by the steps I took long ago when summertime still lingered—
still—
it's all been slept away

I change but the trolleybus stays
—the graffiti whitened by the rain and childhood stains
of chocolate milk—
the homelessness braided in hair
—it's just the wine that's new
and all the sorrows unlived
that reel in the hour before I collect my heaviest bones
and go back to the West—

it's been children born
since I last heard the murmur of women
bringing light to the cemeteries
—since I couldn't understand why I sometimes wake up dead
in a room lit by the sounds of passing trains—

I can read the weather here
—nowhere else—
but it's been autumns warmer every year
since I had someone to tell that
when the dawns are red
it will rain

Katarína Novotná

The Way Prague Hates

do we walk?
do we—
walk all the way from the Old Town
up and up the bones of men lost
        in the heart-fights
        in the fingers stuck inside her cheeks
        in the smell of her wrists
do we walk?
do we even—
walk across the hips of Vltava's bridges
we kiss we kiss we—
        runaways with feet dangling
        from the railway overpass
we dig our nails into her back
until she descends from the hills as mist
Petřín not in sight anymore and
        we kiss we kiss we—
—kiss
and our Madonna crucified
in the faces of beggars in metro transfer tunnels
her beauty stuck to the soles of dirty bare feet
do we walk from A to B?
do we—
walk from A
to the morning after we bit her curbs
and we do
we walk over the tram tracks
under the bridge and home
swarms of souls closing behind our backs
        elbows out
we need to leave a trail of crumbs
or she swallows us whole
and only spits the shoes out

Katarina Novotna

Sex Pink Moon

Sarah Maria Griffin

Hades gave Persephone a pomegranate. Stop me if you've heard this one before.

Persephone was the daughter of Demeter and Zeus, the queen and king of the gods of ancient Greece. Hades showed up one day on his chariot and whisked her away and her mother was so heartbroken that she stopped all the plants and trees from growing in Persephone's absence and went down to the gates of hell to rail and roar and demand her return.

Hades wasn't feeling it. He agreed to let Persephone go, but not without slipping her a pomegranate as a parting gift. Eating the fruit of the underworld, especially the fruit that Hades himself puts in your hand, comes with a price—Persephone was by the taste of it tied to the underworld, and had to return to Hades for a third of the year, every year. This is why we have winter: because the plants and trees die every time she goes away.

The first time I see a pomegranate I am in a crowded Financial District meeting room in San Francisco with fifty other women. I see it in the hands of the redhead beside me as we sit: it is notable that we sit because there are many women standing, softly shifting their weight from one foot to another, almost jogging in place—or dancing listlessly to a tune only they can hear. Each movement is something burned from their bodies. But we sit. Me and the girl with the pomegranate. The pink jewels in membrane come away in her fingers, a cracked open orb in a Tupperware box. I have no idea what it is but if she's eating it in here, it must be good, it must be approved of, it must be free. You couldn't just sit here eating in front of the standing, swaying women, unless somehow the thing you were eating was as virtuous as exercise. I want to know its name, so I can go and get one for myself, add it to my list of permitted foods.

We listened to the thin woman at the front of the room every Tuesday and then we lined up to get weighed. We got a sticker if we had lost something. I loved the stickers, I loved the gradually receding coastline of my body. It was just the hunger I couldn't stand.

Sarah, the girl beside me, eventually offers me some of the fruit because I am half-staring, and laughs—not unkindly—when I ask what it is. Americans do this when I reveal that I have never eaten foods that are commonplace to them, when I refuse to pretend that I have assimilated and wear my otherness without shame. I take their laughter, because I know it is a small price to pay for safe passage.

She passes me a little cluster of ruby seeds, still clinging to the interior scaffolding of the fruit. I pluck one and it bursts in my mouth, bright and tart. I eat the others, too, like tiny candies. How have I shared a planet with these things for so long and never known this sweetness? Better, this permitted sweetness, this sweetness that comes with no price? She nods when I ask if it's free to eat, and says, 'You can have as many as you want.' I thank Sarah and thumb the membrane between my fingers, too scarlet to ask for more, but determined to find one of my own on my way back home.

After this I see them everywhere. The sex pink moon of the pomegranate manifests itself in supermarkets, on menus, in conversation. It has always been there, just never in my orbit, but now it sits in my skyline, full.

It feels strange and humiliating to admit that I have attended weight-loss programmes. Admitting this kind of participation in a very patriarchal breed of capitalism does not feel feminist, it feels like a failure. All this, and the truth of it is that I have tried to lose weight by eating what a company told me to. I paid these companies and they handed me the spellbook and I charmed myself and my plates in the hope that my body would shrink. This feels like revealing a profound flaw in how I handle my self-loathing. It feels like admitting I woke up one day and my body was not my body, rather some strange island I washed up on without a map. It feels like raised hands to a world of brutal, impossible beauty standards, a white flag to the trained male gaze. It feels like I should be smarter, like I should intellectualise myself into a certain peace with my body.

At the time of writing, in the dense summer flat of a heatwave, this is the longest I have gone without joining a programme in eight years.

My twenties were defined by pursuit of thinness and crushing, repeated failure. Due to wild bouts of depression—something I did not for a long time have any language to describe—my body changed again and again, against my will and my willpower. Hunger and excess lie in each of my palms and both of them are pomegranates: sweet, heavy things that I could barely identify until long past my teens. The truth is that I have, in my life, lived in a body that has shifted in ways that mean I am mystified looking at photographs of myself during the last decade. Nobody ever really said much about it: they let me starve, they let me swell. This underworld was mine to navigate and there were no search parties coming, just myself at the door whispering through the letterbox, 'Do you want to feel like this for the rest of your life?' It is not that I wanted to be congratulated on loss—though I was, sometimes, because the world we live in unfairly rewards the shrinking body. Congratulations on all the hunger, the counting, the exhaustion, you look like you've dropped a dress size. That, I didn't want. I think I just wanted someone to ask if I was okay.

I am not sure that there is anything political about my current body size: in fact, there was little or nothing political about it when it was larger, or smaller. I am a medium-sized creature in the world who does not slot neatly into binary conversations about bodily representation. Fat bodies are punished, thin bodies rewarded—bodies in between occupy a liminal and often privileged space. There is potentially no conversation that even needs to be had about my body: I am in many regards invisible. A little taller than most people. Mostly pretty healthy, bar a bad back and somewhat mysterious kidneys. I am writing from a place of the deeply, invisibly average. This is the only point I can write from; I can't claim to speak from any other size or place. Just from here, in the space in between.

This in mind, joining a weight-loss programme—then failing out, then re-joining again—was a mundane surrender. In the grand scheme of the systemic battles that we fight daily as women, did this truly matter? The deep red marks in my hips or the tracks from denim seams on my thighs or the fact that I did not keep a full-length mirror in my home for five years—were these not petty, small problems of privilege? I had been told again and again that there was nothing more boring than listening to a woman talking about trying to lose weight, so I didn't do it. I promised myself during the eight years that I attended meetings in grey rooms full of nameless women, that this bit belonged to me. The meticulous counting was mine. The long, burning walks that earned me extra points, or just a little less guilt, were mine. My head down in meeting rooms, my fists full of pomegranate seeds. These were mine. This failure was mine.

In New York City, in the Metropolitan Museum of Art, a piece entitled the *Unicorn Tapestries* hangs in eight parts. Nobody knows who wove it; it dates from the Medieval period, which means it was probably designed and constructed by a collection of French women whose names are long lost to history. The sequence depicts the taming and capture of a beast. Even the word 'unicorn' has lost the wonder it previously held: the creature is no longer just mythological, now an emoji, a t-shirt design. In the seventh of the eight images, 'The Unicorn in Captivity', a pomegranate tree stands in the center of a lush green meadow, and tied by the neck to the trunk is a unicorn. The legendary beast sits under the boughs, tamed, thighs stained with pink juice from the bursting fruit above. The unicorn is satisfied. It does not want to leave, though it couldn't if it tried. A happily bound creature.

Here's a secret. During the period in which this tapestry was woven, there were no pomegranates in France. The tree was depicted with no knowledge of the reality of the fruit, just whisper and myth. The women who wove this image had never seen a pomegranate tree: a thing as mythological to them as the unicorn tied to the trunk. Still, the story made sense. The pomegranate kept the unicorn happy. It was enough.

In my time I have willingly been bound to two trees, I have stepped into two hells by choice. One was Slimming World, the other Weight Watchers. Their vocabulary and their treatment of nourishment, plates, ingredients—their matrices of rules—are still in my daily interactions with food, though I do not go out to get weighed by them. They have crept into me, seeded there.

In Slimming World, the shadow-twin of Weight Watchers, you lose what weight you want to lose through the limitation of fat intake. The idea is, the less fat you take in, the more of your body's stored fat gets burned day to day—or so the husky-voiced group leader here in a suburb in Dublin tells us as we sit in a circle around her. We do, of course, have to have a certain amount of these naughtier foods a day, or the whole thing won't work. She assures me there is delicate, considered science here, but to be frank, I am not here to learn science. I am here to lose weight. Besides, she says, we'd all lose our minds if we denied ourselves a cheeky single measured glass of wine or a children's sized ice cream or a low-fat one-hundred-calorie fudge brownie less than the diameter of the palm of your hand, wouldn't we? These thimbles of wine and other miniature treats are measured out to us in the unfortunately named 'syns'. Synthesis Foods, the group leader and the information books insist. Funny little coincidence, that.

The propaganda of the weightloss industry speaks to us in terms of temptation and sin. Our sinful bodies. To be fat is to be impure, to be weak to sweetness and luxury, to bear the evidence of excess. Bones now, they're white, aren't they? Clean. They're one of the first signs of weight loss, for me. A more defined jaw. A collarbone. Eventually, a spine.

Over my twenties, I have participated in both groups. The portion-control-oriented Weight Watchers, the fat-restriction-focused Slimming World. I lose around a stone, usually, then become less anxious. I maintain the loss, then, eventually, am so much at peace that I begin to eat and drink without fear. I swell again. I wake up one morning and decide to return, normally around a year later. I lose, I become happy, I gain, I become anxious, I go back to the realm of the pomegranate and I tie myself to the tree. I ask myself questions with the rope around my neck. I think, am I a bad feminist for this kind of participation? If the bright, brave women I admire find out that I do this to myself, will they judge me—will they believe me stupid for this compliance? Will I be sent out of my coven into the world because I am ungrateful for what I have, a healthy body that grants me the highest of privileges in this world available to a woman? Shouldn't I know better, shouldn't I just love my body regardless of its size, is it not truly radical to refuse the patriarchal gaze that demands my thinness, my hunger? Here I find some of my most personal struggles politicised: here I find myself failing not only as a woman in the patriarchy, but as a feminist railing against it. I only have the admission that I do not know how to correctly be a body in this world: and in that, I don't know how to talk about being a body in the world, either.

I stop using olive oil and mayonnaise, I stop drinking pints. I put hot sauce on everything, I only drink whiskey on ice. Every time I stand on the scale at a meeting and lose, I am losing some weight from my body, sure. However, I feel I would lose the respect of my peers, if they knew.

Here's another secret. I started an Instagram account without my name on it to document what I was eating every day, syn by syn, free portion by heaped, free portion. The images feature acres of broccoli.

Tins upon tins of Heinz Spaghetti Hoops. Almost every single day for breakfast, exactly one slice of bread with the crusts cut off, a portion of mushy peas and enough sriracha to start a small house fire. There are oblique hashtags across the digital expanse, ciphers that signal an account's participation in the program: signs to other participating women that the meals chronicled here are within the rules, maybe something they themselves can emulate. I will not write the many hashtags here: it would feel like a betrayal to the hundreds and thousands of women who live in these secret annals of social media, like me, under anonymous accounts where our bodies and faces do not appear. Just our meals, how we navigate hunger and rise past temptation and still feed ourselves.

The plates in the images that fill these hashtags—millions of plates—are seldom shot beautifully. They are just smartphone snaps of overflowing plates made under the strict but simple tenants of the Slimming World handbook. There are often lots and lots of vegetables: cauliflower florets framing spaghetti bolognese, the sauce full of mushrooms and laced with cubes of carrot. Fat, rugged chips made in the oven with a strange, bastardised oil replacement in a spray can instead of shining, malevolent olive oil, and coated liberally with paprika and celery salt. Here is how you still eat, somehow, each picture says. Here is how you stay full. Here, I am doing this too. No, I will not tell you my name.

The secrecy is part of this underworld club of women bargaining their meals away: the secrecy somehow abides by the truth that while we are doing this to fit better in a world that elevates and values thin bodies and shames fat ones, we are also doing this for ourselves. How can something exist in the space between self-care and obedience to brutal, dangerous cultural norms? What does this mean to the lines of dancing Persephones in the South of Market meeting rooms in San Francisco, the faceless women who chronicle their meals and losses and struggles in those coded hashtags on Instagram—all of whom are real women, whole people with inner lives and personal histories and intelligence and power and kindness. They are just living their lives, enacting their personal quests for peace with their bodies—or a bargain with the patriarchy—or wherever those two things meet and become one. I am at once a participant and a voyeur. In judging them, I judge myself. When does this become disordered, when does this pursuit of control turn and control us? Does the secrecy just make it worse, a collusion of hungry women, thighs red with pomegranates juice, bound, but content? At least these women have one another to talk to, free from the confessions we are told are boring, or worse, oppressive. Is this semi-public journalling of diet disordered, or is it orderly, or is there some space in the margins for which we do not yet have a critical feminist language? I am not sure I can see it objectively, because I've waded through those mires, I have the stains on my skin, I have been tied to the tree. I find myself with only questions, not answers—the interrogation of the body and loss and gain is not one that just ends, rather one that spawns.

My mother joined Weight Watchers when I was a child. My godmother was the first to pass me photocopied-and-stapled-together pirated Slimming World information booklets when I asked for them, discontent and a stranger in my own skin. I think about how hard both of these women work, how their lives and mine are intrinsically woven together—how our faces match, our bodies match, especially as I grow older. I think they are both Demeter, they are both Persephone. They are both busy, and kind, and supportive. They are vocal feminists, my mother a campaigner. I do not know their lives in their bodies: that is not my story to tell. I only know that I have the same nose as them, the same architecture of bones. I do know that I don't consider them traitors for their counting of points and syns. In fact, I feel a rabid fury in my chest at the thought of anyone making judgements about them in this regard. Perhaps I am Demeter too.

There is a restaurant in San Francisco, somewhere in the cross-section of the Mission and Bernal Heights, called The Front Porch. It is a long, dark cavern where buttermilkfried chicken comes in buckets littered with oily, salty popcorn—where the Bloody Marys have diced bacon around the lip of the glass, where I discovered a wild taste for deep-fried okra and a loathing of grits. It is where all your syns come home to roost, where your points lay themselves out on the menu and render themselves pointless. I did not last long in Weight Watchers that year, and would throw myself at this altar of oil and seasoning and new tastes and love every second of it, the fullness that came with such indulgence, the spectacle of soul food, how profoundly opposite to the plates of my childhood each turn here was. My husband and I would sit at brunch time, listening to Nirvana roar foggily over the sound system in the darkened booths and get drunk too early in the day, coasting through a menu of delicious harm, wondering what the hell we were doing in America other than eating ourselves numb and working ourselves to death.

The cocktail I would order with my breakfast—most often, a duck confit and sweet potato hash crowned with two outrageous, golden eggs fried in butter—was called the Persephone. The ingredients were simple: prosecco, pomegranate molasses, and a twist of orange peel to garnish. It was served in a champagne coupe and the molasses would gather heavy at the bottom, like clotted blood. I could have as many as I wanted: this sweet fruit belonged to me and perhaps I would pay for it when the time came, but until then I just tilted my head back and drank. I would down one after another after another.

Parallel of Past Imperfect

Clare Archibald

Vascular

There is a walk. Within the borders of your county, in lines that you have not traced, you go. It is advertised as a social walk, as a re-enactment of the pilgrim way, and something to do with Ben Jonson. You arrange to go with your most equivalently not really misanthropic friend so that neither of you feel alone whilst pretending to be consistently social of requisite. You hear of the witches of Fife who were flung under stone in mudflats of social suction and wonder about the instruments of torture, real and of the mind, to determine stratified truths. Pass sheds that peel off time with their absorption by coast of weather. Spot berries that remind you of cellular data stored somewhere within. Frozen in territorial time. *Who has the right to take the picture?* You feel uncomfortable. You are used to walking alone or with one other variable person of choice who happens to look at different things. Should you reach for the green polka dot dress before they buy it. Hide in the corner of the changing room. Will it look better on them anyway because they understand the theory of sewing and wearing and not just the feel of it, the lichen that just is. You walk and talk of none of this. Feel furtive in your dipped fronds of wantings. Self-conscious in your actions of intended you are watching yourself as the watcher, flooding your mind with brake fluid. It builds and bubbles and froths corrosion at your daydreams.

The Second Person You

When all that is there falls into the after you plunge with it in skirmish of self. Simultaneous traces of

blunted polished broken expansive corroded isolated melded

confirmed edges of you appear in colours

seeping from eyes

folding with grey of always known but never seen.

Routes

You are neither a nomad nor a pilgrim. You are unsure if you look to affirm or negate or with no apparent reason. In seeing you feel the movement of unworded on your tongue. The answer to can you touch your eyeballs with your tongue is always no. To which you both agree and disagree. You are a swirl of outlines that merge in points of tip.

You find yourself in the place that you live more often than expected. Perhaps you begin to dwell there. Eyes and body are opened more fully to the discovery. On days when your waters are stagnant and flood your mouth with before, you roam the virtual world where you can participate without pretending to be. Photographs on a screen are distended reminders of parts of long ago that bring life to the present. Existence of future you.

You have no thought of how you are seen by others because you do not yet believe again in possibilities of future. When you are undammed from stasis perhaps you no longer care.

Except you do.

You know this because you have stood on a beach and silently mouthed your lexicon of self.

You know this because you have tossed the words in salivate and spat them on eyeballs to see if they sting in spirals or syncopated lines.

You can sink into other people's sockets, curl into position as an unfurled fern of hidden knowing and look as in hum of static.

You do this perhaps because you want your eye to speak your soul in order to find out if you have one.

It makes you aware of how you look if not how you are seen.

There is no shuttering or enclosure, words smear the photographs you take with the you of unreplicate.

Eyes polish them with stones of others and their way of seeing until all is absorbed in acts of seen and said that are not catharsis or copy.

Do you believe that contemplation is not feeling?

The Collective I

You are sent his book that looks from hill to sea by an individual man of psychogeography who is a collective in the truest sense of spirit. In watching him look in virtual duplication of the real, his way of seeing has shown you that your eyes of own are not faulty and that you like the word inherent. In the acknowledgements he thanks you amongst others and says you may not know why. You do not. And this acceptance of unknowing is your reciprocation. On the day of walking reality, you walk at self conscious intersections and you listen to his local knowledge of ways.

After lunch at a village pub where the others sing traditional songs whilst you and your friend drink pints of Guinness in homage to no-one except your buds of taste: you walk on. You are struck by folded white clothes in a window and linger to take an image that for unquantifiable reasons has made you bold. You finish and turn into a country lane and there lies Dead Car Alley.

You have no idea why you call it this as the immediate response in both your mind and body tells you they are very much alive. You hear a silent hum of your choosing as you see two others crouch and photograph with reflected animation. Feel the ricochet of rust enliven them but you walk on. Much later you read Susan Sontag's *On Photography* and her thought that 'beauty requires the imprint of a human decision' and you think that your decision to walk on served to reinforce the beauty because you wanted to see it for yourself, unhampered by the eyes of others, not wanting to edge into their locus of vision so that they may see unblurred in dance of desire lines of sight.

You could say that as you walked that the lane undulated with apparently strewn cars, many unseen until the next visit, and the one thereafter. Accumulation of visits culminating in an almost end point of these words. You could spiral and spin and birl and fossilise them forever or you could contain them within a square and test their kilter. You could redirect the flow to the shortest route of meaning or do as Agnes Martin did and raze all other options and make the flow your own in small acts of mourning.

Could count the ferns growing among them whispering secret spores of past lives. But you don't. Could choose your own beginning that is also the end. You could put words under above these pictures and have people tell you they are extended captions but you do not like the word and it does not express what you are implying, which is perhaps nothing. You invoke only the cartwheels of self that allows you to unword the words. Only much later do you learn that caption is intellectual shorthand for having read Walter Benjamin, Berger and others. This makes you question your instinct of intuitive bias as pre-ingested foreknowing of the subconscious, and your eyelids lower.

Do you believe in serendipity of instinct or intellect?

Instinct made verbal streams out words of glints and traces in flow and flux of merge and syncopate. Words that you read later in books and wonder whose they are.

And if the words are not yours where do feelings belong.

You are taught by others without their knowledge. You are seen by others without your knowledge. You isolate these thoughts in skew of straddle and move on.

You all walk on past the cars and handful of houses up the lane and are seemingly equally struck by the sun sky soil shapes of the field. This is psychically permitted as a universally acknowledged picture. It is not so-called ruin porn or chromatic fragmentation. It is simple beauty and not a decisive act of intervention in the flow. Do you despise the word trope? Struggle with the word beauty? Feel shy of your eye?

Some barns are held up by rolls of hay whose contours shadow everything a wild cornflower blue and the woman with whom you are walking—who can see you see it—says she much prefers to take pictures alone. You do an inward dance of saying in agreement and feel free.

You go home and later the singular person of the collective posts his image of another blue, the vibrant blue of a dying car, and you relish the unatrophied resplendence of it as seen by another.

Gather

Thoughts of Dead Car Alley seep and lurk inside for months. You think that you may have said you will write about it and the individual collective kindly did not, to leave you the space to do so, but you do not know how to negotiate this terrain and may have imagined this in rehearsal.

Weather the thoughts and see what happens. Taste the corrugated lick and drip of someone else's edges. You are unschooled in the academic words and the intellectual ways and rely in the truest sense on instinct. Your propulsion is just that in growing spirals of zoom, crop, zoom, crop, lick. You are a Venn diagram of not quite anything and perhaps this is why you taste the cars leach without words.

You wonder about the cars and what they mean. You could search online to see if there have been complaints to the council but you don't. Perhaps the cluster of houses on the lane rotates inwardly around hoarded acts of spoken or unspoken aspiration or failure. Neighbours might campaign about the anti-social behaviour of decomposing dreams by their lawns. You have an online conversation about the wonder and talk of how you might go back and chap the door because you agree with John Berger: 'there is an element of curiosity in shyness. It's to do with daring. That's the paradox. It's the adventurous who are shy.'

Coiled

You go back to the beginning and return. Not to the actual beginning of the walk but to the real beginning for you: the window of clothes and the turn of the corner into Dead Car Alley and you think about Pina Bausch and the dance of spectate and repetition that can never be true. In true ironic mimesis of cars that cannot drive neither do you, so ask your friend to take you. He does and finds a tree that he likes.

Later you find out that the individual of the collective also returned, the day before you in fact, and this act of almost synchronicity makes you smile. You wonder about the improved quality of experience and images for the unselfconscious. You share a place of silent solidarity on the sliding scale of unvoiced minor explorations.

He does not chap the door and neither do you.

zoom crop zoom crop all is reduced to lines of lead given the independence of transcendence. ZOOM CROP ZOOM CROP all is weathered by personally imposed narrative.

Instead you stare and reduce, stare and expand. See detail spore in front of you. You feel added sides of the puzzle as the geometry of cars grows ever more present in the code of shaping. You are taking a photograph of the rain ripped insides of a previously unnoticed car when a man appears. He seems curious but friendly and you hope his eyes mirror this in you. He visibly takes a mental snapshot of the situation and approaches you with unspoken question. You catch his eye as it touches on the car and feel his connection to them vibrate. His cars are beautiful you tell him, say that although you don't drive and have no interest in cars you have been thinking about them since you encountered them the first time. Encounter is the correct term. You surprise yourself by having thought he might have a gun. You feel the silhouette of assumption and imposition bulge free from your eyes. You are scared he might cry and tell you of a dead wife and how his life and time stopped, that his grief is embodied in the unrestrained silent transition of the cars. You feel advance guilt at forcing him to excavate his past and present to unearth how this lane of cars can be.

He contorts your expectations as he talks you through the cars, breathing them emphatically as a project that is very much alive. He tells you that he has another in the garage that he is working on. He shares his imaginings of them, when they will be like new again, as if that were possible, and you wonder if he will think that recovery will also be a loss. You now have dates of when they were new and he lets you take more photographs of the marks of organic life inside and out. He points at one that has been in the same spot waiting to be fixed since 1972 and you marvel. At him, at the cars' irrefutable presence in all tenses, and the ability of those you see walking by with dogs and children not to notice. You would like to ask him more questions but the line is invisible and you have already skipped around with it.

After 1, 2, 3, visits you think of Agnes Martin and tone over colour, rectangle over square, weaving of thought and seeing and you feel the generosity of spirit of those who share their connections of mind and body as they trace their outlines allowing kilter of others. You laugh at Agnes in her cabin with no water, miles from human contact, preserving her sports car as trophy of freedom, of hard won solitude. You would like to think that she would laugh back at you for seeking to isolate personal words as universal.

Swirl / Spray

You sit on your beach of remade structures and question the placing of your words. You think of decomposing memories of blood, muscle, ash, water, bone. Swill of before in gristle of after.

You notice the edges of unknown others, the flowers randomly but precisely placed, the half crying half celebrating families in smart clothes walking away from the water at its most private, flowers strategically placed to rot, wither and merge in unseen acts of beauty.

After 1, 2, 3 visits you see new shapes in the sand.

You have been back to Dead Car Alley for a third time and cannot shift the automatic title although you know it not to be true. You were driven once more in an act of pedestrian dichotomy. This time there is no human touch of intervention and you are left alone to look. This time though you can see his face hover and it alchemises the experience of looking. The cumulation of cars unseen continues. You count two additional. Your lines of seeing reinterpret previous reductions. There is no chaos. The cars are all neatly parked beside well-tended human habitats; there is a noted absence of fused leaf metal hanging in mercurial tendrils on public pathways. Romanticised presence of decay is not here. Instead there is demarcation. You walk between tidy thoughts of hope and previously held despair and wonder about personal responses to what we make public, public reactions to what we make personal. The cause and effect calculation means that you have hundreds of photographs of his cars, some of your favourites you will not use because they have numbers of tracking, of identification and this would be imposition. You like the word intervention but this is defiantly not it.

Absorption

The public sand is gouged out with words of private memorial. If appearances have their own language then this one mouths with forceful unsilence. You feel conflicted in your recognition of the rhythm of R.I.P. and your rejection of its meaning. You hear the sea unable to read the public words of we love you always, its waves unseeing of the balloon and plastic flower that it will swallow to muffle the identity of mum, the adjective wonderful, a woman lost in anonymity twice over. You took a picture after you made the decision to intervene. You stood between sea and grief and chose the hidden life of the waves. You moved the balloon and plastic flowers that would never be fully watered down. You removed the presence of their thoughts without knowing who they were. So you took a picture to preserve the tableau and to demonstrate a level of deference that you felt emotionally constructed to feel. You took a picture to avoid feeling angry at the thoughtlessness of the blurring of boundaries of dead and damage to living, and then you left the scene.

You wondered about all the secret words that have been buried there by your own eyes and moved to places of public by your mouth and fingers. You thought about your words of dead babies and no ashes to throw in the sea with fake or appropriately environmentally dying flowers and you felt glad that you had circumnavigated some boundaries in real life if not on paper.

You will keep the picture to show perhaps only yourself that you did not walk casually over the dead of unknown others, and the memorial of anonymous will have a future in parallel with its other ways of continuing to be. Until it is perhaps deleted. Or forgotten.

Whirr

You send a photograph from the book *On Photography* to a friend, without comment because further verbs and adjectives are superfluous. Later, a musician who writes with his eye from inside and out , and whose images from his often above the clouds parachute into your timeline with quietly felt landing, posts the same picture. Of the same chapter that simply says 'On Melancholy'. You laugh at the thought of chords being struck and comment online that you also took and sent this picture. You joke that there is potential for a book about the photographs taken of this page but think seriously about the iconography of words.

Another musician is missing. You did not know his words but have friends who know them, and you know of the mass devotion. You listen to his words for the first time and look out at your sea which flashes granite of landing on its false curves. He wrote about floating down your sea and you listen and are choked with the inhale of others. There are many searches, real and online. You look out at the sea and try not to imbibe the unusual sound of the water as the helicopters accompany the irregular pattern of the lifeboats. You see the churn of others but can only now fully see the procession of solitary shoe soles washed up in mud. Flat evidence of material unknown. You remember the time you saw him sat at the beach wall looking out at this sea and now you look at the waves and cannot unsee the toss of all that is contained. You think of the cars and the longings and despair that cannot be held in sentences by others. You think of his words that hold others in echo of him and watch the flowers of memory crack through the concrete of the sea and think of the oddness that at least for his family there is a body of knowing.

You think of Anselm Kiefer and the red berries of vision appear again to remind you of his thinking that no atom is ever lost. You wonder if there is ever really such a thing as infertile landscapes and sometimes walk willingly with others to understand thresholds of disintegration and formation. You contemplate if you can create chaos of liberation in words. You zoom crop zoom crop and all reduction is expansiveness of feeling. You summoned your nature in Dead Car Alley and you are enlivened by the eyes of other and the applicable tenses of knowledge now dance in shapes of you.

The View from Mostowa Street

I.

At the café window, the prospect of snow
seems endless. Clouds detour sunlight,
shadows work the walls of tenements.
At my feet, sacks of herring and black bread
that a spinster—fingerless gloves, smoke-yellow
nails, sold me in the marketplace.
Only one other patron here: a pensioner,
frowning at the evening paper
as if it were a love letter etched in vanishing ink.

II.

The waitress serves me wormwood liqueur,
binds back her autumn hair. Shirt cropped
at the ribs, she shows me the blue
sparrow tattooed on her hip, swears
it floats above her in her sleep.
Outside, the onset of heavy snow.
It angles off the boulevard, gets snared
in contrary winds. A woman races
into a doorway. A sliver of light escapes.

Jeffrey Alfier

The Blue Slip Sway

Katie Burnip

I always return to the blue slip, with a sway. But things do grow in my body. Faint, but foreboding things. I have a sweet face. I'm very Belle De Jour, this way. Gently violent. A steak knife beneath a lilac pillow. A garter lined with snow. Pink slippers with a trace of yellow at the heel. I'd requested both coffin and carriage for my thirteenth birthday, but returned with a Vienetta instead. My mother'd called me exotic. Miss'd called my manner, my doodles, faux naif. Pink bonnet meek with a hard blue castle in her mouth; something splinter big, but militant, in my gut. It's all about gracious subtlety.

I've been orally fixated since birth. The rattle; the spade. The stick figures I drew were always open mouthed, and multicoloured. Always fixing each other. Big neon hair; bold dresses; a hammer at a girlfriend's face. Viciously practical. The reddy brown scribble above these figures gave the impression of something sacramental; the faces seemed to kneel at it, in supplication.

I loiter by the chopping board, leaning. I sway. I love to-ing, don't you? I hate fro-ing. This place has a chandelier. It's a remarkable feat of human nature. I feel relief beneath it. I'm always looking up at these occasions. It's the Apollonian logic of a simple, square ceiling; the spectacle of a five fingered pentagon hanging heavy, but defiant, from the centre. You've seen this wardrobe? These heavy coats; leather jumpsuits; wired, circular flounces, curled flat and hung an inch off the carpet. They're all compressed and contained by a series of simple yet remarkable contraptions, like us.

Julia makes the comment with quiet pleasure every time: Hannah is not thinking; she's ordered the chowder again. She enjoys big death in my bowl; any stench and disorder upturned, and wafting across my face. She's the soft onion you have to brave before you reach the the drain.

When I hear him say my name, I scan for the other Hannah. I'm hopeful, this way. George fell in love with this lost look. When my name is called I glance left and right, before lurching, as if I've discovered an ingenious method for clearing my ears. My hair is still wet when he leaves the house.

Here's the pink suit with the paired flounce. Under the flickering chandelier, she breathes. I had a friend at drama school with my name, who'd decided to try her hand as a stripper. She required a more generous form of sublimation, a jolting, quick fix. I was begging for it. I needed her to quit clinging. She was always teething on my things.

The two images always merge when I'm at the dos. I strip off the flounce as a healthy young woman. It brings on a physiological response that makes it difficult to hear glasses chink together; the sudden laughter. The cradle rocking in the next room.

This is Frances, with her sixth husband. I'm always happy to be at the table with Frances. She couldn't justify a strip off anywhere, not even within the confines of a dark wardrobe. What a relief.

I want to inspect her up close, but she conceals everything in buttoned up cardigans and bolted jackets. I know of her genius solely through these men. Each one has been slightly better than the last. We share a sandwich each evening. When she leaves her crusts, I can expect a decision has been made. Unaffectedly, she'll begin tracing the window sill, my fork, some fabric. I wish Peter were braver. He's smart, eccentric, but he's no brave cat. Three weeks later, she has a fearless husband who purrs. Frances is a striver; a conqueror; and she manages all this in a grey turtleneck.

George, then me, then twenty-eight years of marriage. He has deceitful thoughts, and they're projected in these orgiastic scenes: each year he gathers people round to celebrate our private intimacy.

I wish that Julia would kiss him. I feel that her splayed cutlery is an indication of a lack of bravery. Go on. She always leaves her potatoes. Halfway through a chat, she runs a finger around the lip of her glass; forgetting to look at the potatoes for comfort. That's why she's unnecessarily faint; why her tantrums are all elbows and knees.

She demands the waiter to leave her plate, as if to say: take a good look. Faceless hunchbacks lying prone in the cold, brown swamp of your marriage. She doesn't know what we're supposed to look like. She taught a young jailer to waltz.

She's interested in George's telling of how we met. Frances couldn't care less. Her husband is feeding her a roast. He's got the airplane method down pat. Each flight from the plate is unique; each piece has better functionality than the one before. Corn hover like bees; slices of meat dive, landing on some remote part of her that she can't reach without physical exertion. Such a tease. Soon, her cutlery kiss, and her plate is cleared. It's like these foolish games never happened.

It's like this: I slow dance alone in a blue dress. Just sway back and forth; the same blue dress, night and day. He returns to me, from far-off places, to find me swaying. Julia is glad I'm wearing a blue dress in every scene. It brings her relief. She's always wearing new colours, new designs, brave or discreet patterns. You never know what you're going to get. I turn the catalogue over and over, and there she is, wearing a different skirt, lounging on a new sofa, jumping for a new ball, in a new garden, with new children. Little does she know, it's not how you fall in love. It's about, each day, opening the same page.

He can be rude. Says sweet things while pointing left and right. It's a trick; a tease. My years as a waitress taught me that the gesture of an upturned palm is less abusive, no matter the customer you're serving. When he points this way, I raise my eyebrows. I look away. Julia is no brave friend.

Let's draw the pink flounce skirt from the hanger, once, twice. You see? She always returns them: you're no retired clitoris, she says. Not yet. What do you think? That's why the hangers always swing back and forth, then jolt still. I know what you think. But this is one of very few gestures she makes nowadays. This dress. The contraceptive taken with trepidation, at six in the morning, while George stirs up trouble in the bathroom. He's always writing out invitations for our next anniversary. In these moments, she approaches as an insubstantial flicker. Then you arrive, Sir.

This was the panama hat I wore to and from school, irrespective of the weather, indoors or out. Like a guinea-pig, I stored these counterintuitive habits in my cheeks. I felt the comfort of a smart smile. Smiles on young girls are foolish, unintelligent. They smile while they sing about death. For me, it was a stock of all the things I'd have to unlearn later.

But, give her her dues, she's always been sensible, reasonable, presentable. She tells me: wear this hat; wear this dress. She's suffocating, but scrupulous. The first time I'd felt her waver, I was returning from the choir. I'd felt relief. Then, I'd felt loveless.

I'd spotted a cake that was garnished in chocolate flowers. I said, go on, eat them. That chocolate cake was only the beginning of me. I felt high over myself. It was the lying. You ate the cake, said Miss. I did not eat the cake, Miss. I knew, lying or no lying, the consequences would be the same. Both God and lying require an exceptional imagination: but I'd been conditioned to expect the same pink-headed Christian, regardless. What a bore.

Often, I'd look at him and think: kneel at his feet, with your palms flat on his knees. Change the outcome. But this hat kept landing on my head. Sorry do gooding thing; so the outcome was always the same: his appropriated biblical references reiterated on the blackboard about sheep and shepherds.

As George's general associate, she keeps me in line. Each time the flounce remains on the hanger. They both know so little about me, and the notion that arbitrary morality is the only kind that exists. You know how good I became; on what amicable terms she and I were on, when I left his office, beaten, dishevelled and damp faced. Then look who returns…

Of course, when, after dinner, I am putting lotion on my hands, and he is leaning against the door, I look at my husband's reflection, and I feel that he definitely knows me. In this blue slip, she feels content to disappear. So do you. I strike some balance for all of us…

I've seen this theme recur many times, in film: there is discord everywhere, except the marriage.

After I have taken off my earrings, and laid them on the bedside table, I apply lotion (always to the hands.) I make a dive for the chest. Will we discuss our son's failures at the chess board? The fact that our daughter is too thin? Do we, then, agree that more potatoes at dinner might help her situation? All is done for; we've dived through the bed like Olympic swimmers. But we rise to the surface, to touch.

There is something solid in this ideal; these moments are worth making a ritual of. Some semblance of constancy that yields reprieve, and a customised idiosyncrasy, within that ritual. Something minutely animal: a lick of the lobe, a bite of the chin, to give those reasonable people some airtime; to rest oneself backstage, so to speak.

Really, we have no son. No daughter either. We are cleaning up no muck as a team. We are in no rush for children, having ourselves—each in our own right—been miracle births.

We do not contain enough of that protective instinct. Babies are a thing had easily; without struggle; without labour. One thinks them up, and then, during some quiet moment, shared over a nice meal, we swallow them.

Then my daughter is off to formal. It's a frivolous, hurried exit. He doesn't check the fellow is fully stocked with car and corsage, etc. He leaves her at the door and returns to loiter by the toaster, to inspect the sherry. I slam the cup down. Make a shepherdess of me, Sir. His unwarranted surveillance; my theatrics borne of repressed creativity;

our daughter fleeing the house in beige fishnets, while an empty cradle rocks back and forth in the next room with the help of no hand.

But the parts of those scenes that have always bought me reprieve have been the lotion on the hands, and the going to the chest. It's like slipping into a hot bath after a walk in the snow—there is no fear there, only minor ambivalence. The tingle, the expectation of brief suffering, followed by the rise, the fall.

As I've mentioned, George and I were both a surprise, so we take life for granted. He taps his chin with an index finger when he's thinking. He has the gift of being precisely all the things I'd written on my waitering CV. His best attribute, really, is patience: a kind of frantic peace. I understand how these things work, intellectually; but I'm picking daisies while uprooting whole gardens.

He pats his pockets before he leaves the house. It's all about George have you got a spare… can you do… etc. When I dive to the chest, these are his ruminations, spoken with ample concern: people need me; they rely on me; I've got to be at the top of my game. It's like the commentary on an ad for MensMulti: the broad brilliant man, pouring good water into too many glasses.

We were both accident births; each born from pure intentions. The child shits in the sink, then walks away. The mother points to the shit, but the child keeps working on her jigsaw mat. The mother points to this shit, and shouts. We refuse to look at our shit, while sipping warm milk.

My parents can't recall the precise moment when the winning team won at the ugly sport. I'm nearest to being borne of immaculate conception. No sweat, no secretions, can be traced back to me; no memory recalled. I could be the consequence of no act. Hence swaying, so often, by the chopping board, indecisively. I could've fallen into hay, or a soft blanket. Some days I fall into both in close succession.

If Hannah were here, she'd throw cleavage at everybody, not just a brief dip at my husband—she was brave like that. Julia bends over the chowder; just enough time for the steam to begin emanating from her chest. This is the fool we found dancing her way down the dairy aisle, in nothing but a bridal lace curtain. Then later, prostrate beneath the cutlery drawer.

Has he forgotten her splayed out on the kitchen floor and pointing at her baby *for God's sake act like a lady*. The baby cried louder and louder. We'd tried to make an intervention of it. When she stood, all the elements fell from her hair. She'd mistaken them for pick up sticks; began arranging them in colours around the room; stacking them, corner to corner. George'd carried her upstairs, and across threshold. Save me.

Now she's dipping her cleavage at him as if it never happened. How desperate. That's twenty-eight years of marriage. Frances inclines her head toward a dessert at the thought. It's a slow drive through the mud, she says. She breaks the surface with remarkable deliberation.

Let's recall the scene, together, you and I. George and I open it up like a picture book, each night. I smell far-off places on his body. I bite his chin. Where has he been? I look over my shoulder to examine the place.

I look left, then right. He kisses each cheek. I make a dive for the chest. But then there's a slow stir.

I hear the rattle, rattle. The cradle rocks. I swallow, but it keeps rocking. The baby keeps weeping. I swallow, and swallow. Then draws open; and cutlery splay. The choir smiles. Then Hannah strips. She breathes. Taps turn. Endless crusts; Frances scoffs and scoffs, but she keeps on dragging them out the drain. Who next? She says. The chandelier. It flickers above the stench. The hangers swing back and forth. Julia rises. You say the usual. Don't give her the credit. It's George pouring water over the flounce. You still keep drying everything. But he keeps on wetting it; the heavy coats; leather jumpsuits; wired, circular flounces. They to; they fro. I rise; I fall; I return in the blue slip, with a sway.

FEATURED POET

James Patterson is from Newry, Co. Down. Recent publications have included: Hennessy New Irish Writing (*The Irish Times*); *Magma*; *New Statesman*; and *Poetry Ireland Review*. In 2017 he received an ACES bursary from the Arts Council of Northern Ireland. He is working on his first collection.

[ghost estates]

in each of these i picture the dead
wrapped in carrion   as in evening wear
for the gathering of some smart party

        their lips puckered & shrank
rendering silence   their shoes warped
& legs buckled   though carried somehow

with the grace of no longer being
    of separation from the living
    who buy houses they ll never inhabit

with money they ll never accumulate
on time which is speculative
    limited   and never guaranteed

[the drowning]

the story then became like this

then vanished like eurydice

his friends went looking for him there

beneath the rusted excavator

they brought corned beef & bits of soda

they brought some hershey s from the soldiers

and checked the crushers filled with ashlar

decided they would jump in also

and so the parents brought their hammers

and built a mast from railway sleepers

and built a boat to cross the quarry

and followed them into the hollow

and so the Mayor dived for the parents

and so the council braved the currents

and then the doctors & the soldiers

until at last they filled the swimhole

he d jumped in off a clydesdale horse

beneath the sawdust oil & gorse

sun scorched in their wool knit pants

up from high st & the manse

wrapped up in a greaseproof square

some d arcy s kept in earthenware

the morris tipper & the track

when they failed to bring him back

bits of sheathing casing nails

darning suntans for their sails

diving where their kids went in

which locals said had no bottom

worried for his yearly vote

for their leader s anecdote

followed by the entire town

and all of us were underground

[prosopagnosia]

frozen   on the top street in barcroft
    and looking out over the town splayed
on the valley floor below
like a shattered bauble
    i await your call then see the car

our 2004 silver volvo sedan
parked beneath a streetlight
with a man inside
his hands around the steering wheel
like hands around a cracking branch
his face on the inner convex
of the tinted windshield   unshaven
breathing our cherry scented air
and worrying aloud
via speaker phone over the low hum
of the archers on radio four
i worry about coins in the change tray
and jellies in the glove compartment
and wonder if the odometer glowing
in his face might put him off
any notion he has of theft

so I ask getting in   *how are things*
        to which he looks at me nodding
    back to being you
    the seats frayed imitation leather
warming beneath us both
as you carry me home in the dark
    trusting that someone wasn t plagiarising
your creator s blueprints
for a doppelganger
    and that my own creator
remains beside me   driving

[clouds on a screen at a drive in n j 1960]

so then allan & i went to the drive in
in hoboken   mom looked after the kids

        and while we were filling up on gas
and getting candy along the way

i bought a pack of flashbulbs & a pint
of four roses at about the same time

allan was tipping the attendant and telling
him go nowhere stories about the war

        back then he d talk about how family stores
like my dad s were repositories of memories

yet to be made   that each bar of soap sold
    suit made to fit   kitchen set displayed

& dollar tendered was in anticipation
of a life as yet unburdened by collapse

        that photographs too   fulfilled this need
to anthologize and make tangible the fleeting

        so when i tell you the picture we watched
wasn t very interesting   that s because it wasn t

        some old thing by hitchcock about a man
who kills a woman and all the suspense that

that involves   hardly worth the celluloid
        the picture i d take would focus on a crescent

of buicks   fords & cadillacs crouched
around a hovering still life of the moon

    wire strung lanterns strung low over
a picket fence behind a silver screen

    the night sky burned black into the foreground
& allan asleep beside me dreaming   *diane*

[walking by your childhood home]

and next door s marketplace opens
out into the road   the space between cars
ariot with porcelain dolls & mantel ornaments

        our walk impeded by second hand sofas
& paint covered kitchen chairs
        so we climb the back wall to get a better look

and thread our fingers each through
the other s   our digits indistinguishable
in the time it takes to drop to the yard below

    our boots stuck with sleech & snapped twigs
from the river buried long ago
        you note the colour   moving as we do

through bracken to pull boards
from the back entrance   of the walls
    which in this light appear bright sky blue

    and all the window & door spaces
like doors into an elsewhere
        i feel the unwelcome brush of cobwebs

    the breath of accumulated moulds & lichen
    the consecrated damp of the unliving
and illuminated by this thin shaft of light

   we step across the threshold into a dark
where once you sat copying times tables
into an exercise book wrapped in wallpaper

i try to imagine this child you were
but can only reach that dark unknown
between your narrative & mine

through which past is caught and *then*
becomes *now*   and abruptly the house
emerges as a picture on a slide

your *home sweet home* nailed
solid above the front door   sun shining
freely through unmolested windows

i turn again to look at your face
but only see myself   unrecognised   in the eyes
of a child trying to remember why she left

[postscript]

that we could walk hand in hand down a road that neither takes us home   nor ends   nor makes us tired to continue   that the significance of it   i mean to say   hits me freshly each time it dissipates   like breath freed from a pried sarcophagus   or the slipped refrain of an air caught in a bar or on a bus or in a bookshop behind the stacks of *ya* & *sf*   is a possibility which leaves me both terrified & elated   replacing face after face   until everyone's face is yours

The Bank Job

Sean Tanner

The first one, taken about forty minutes ago, hadn't done shit, so Jack doled out another two SpongeBob-shaped pills apiece. Two, instead of the recommended one, because Shane and Gerry were fearful and riled to the point of nausea. Jack knew they wouldn't go ahead with the job unless their nerves had been well and truly fellated. Jack double dropped as well, not that he needed to, but just for the fuck of it.

Jack was riding shotgun, his knee hopping up and down, his fingers drumming the dash. Beside him Gerry gripped the steering wheel and clenched his teeth.

In the back, Shane leaned forward and hunched between the two front seats. He rubbed at his eyes and said, 'Ye getting anything?'

The car-park was empty, save the three lads in the car and a spatter of undying crows that lined the peripherals. They cawed listlessly from telephone poles as an empty Tayto packet went skittering across the lot on the back of a disinterested breeze. The crows watched the shit-box Fiesta and waited for the lads to get on with it.

'I'm getting fuck all,' said Gerry. 'Duds?'

'No chance,' said Jack. 'If anything, they'll be too strong.'

Gerry was alarmed. 'They can't be too strong. We can't go in there off our tits. They were just supposed to keep us calm. Benzos you said. Benzos to keep us calm.'

'Relax, Gerry. Duffer knows what he's about. He's the best chemist I know.'

'He's the only chemist you know, and he's fucked in the head from sampling his own wares to boot.'

'Arra, we're all a bit fucked in the head,' said Jack.

Shane blew out a loud sigh. 'He's right there, Ger. Can't none of us throw the stone on that count—oh-my-goodness, lads. I think I'm getting something. I can feel it in my legs. It always starts in my legs. Mmm, uh-huh, hmmm. Definitely getting a bit floaty here.'

Jack clapped his hands together, rubbing them fiercely. 'Hon, Shaney boi! This is it, fellas. This is fucking it.'

'What's it like?' asked Gerry. 'Is it strong? Is it too strong? Maybe we should stick our fingers down our throats, puke 'em up, like. I don't want to be off my face here. That's the last thing we need.' At twenty-nine, Gerry had a year on his friends, and it was at times like this that he felt the nagging onus of maturity. Not that it ever did them much good, but there it was all the same.

Shane sucked in a fat yogic breath through his nose, and exhaled out his mouth. 'Mmmm, it's alright. Not too strong, not too strong.' Then he groaned, a kind of a nervous whicker. 'But it is a bit strong. It's like, just coming up on yokes or something, you know. Oh lads, maybe it is a bit strong. Coming on me now.' He was pushing the breaths out through pursed lips like a pregnant woman going into labour.

Gerry, whose experience of hard drugs extended to one bad mushroom trip in Amsterdam when he was twenty-one, looked on, his face draining. 'Oh fuck it, Jack. They were only supposed to calm us down. Benzos, Valium or Xanax or something, like, not whatever the fuck is going on here.' He gestured to Shane.

'Woooo!' said Jack, doing a little jig in his chair. 'Buckle up boys. It's going to be a hell of a ride.' Jack drummed the dash and bobbed his head, jiving along to some unheard music. 'Feeling something, fellas. Something going on under the crust. Those tectonic plates be shifting. Continental drift, fellas, subterranean energies surging. Woooo!'

'Woooo!' said Shane throwing his head back like a howling wolf.

'Yes, Shane boi!'

'Yes, Jackie boi!'

Gerry scrunched up his face, pushing his eyeballs into his skull. That first wicked tingle of narcotic glee had begun to tickle the base of his spine. As soon as he felt it, he knew it was too late to go back. Things, he knew, were about to get weird. 'Fuck it,' he said. 'Here we go.'

#

Outside the car, the world was grey and dumb. The immortal crows sat sullen under a sky full of heavy cloud.

The town, Bally-who-gives-a-shit, was quiet and had nothing to say for itself. Weren't many people about the place. The one or two souls they did see popping in and out of the shops didn't trouble to glance in the lads' direction. And if they did, sure what about it? The lads hadn't done anything wrong. They were just a few lads sitting in a car, like. No harm, no foul. Not yet anyway.

Bally was a prissy little shit of a town whose only ambition was to go to work, and listen to teacher, and pay its taxes. The lads hated it almost as much as the crows did. They hated the suburban stink of the place, the cloying civility and the limp-dicked pleasantness of it all. But most of all, they hated the fact that they still lived there, in this dishonest little town. A place so shrinking small when the world was yawning so wide.

Bally's idea of excitement was a young fella found hanging off the big oak in the tidy towns' millennial garden. Or some young wan raped behind the tidy towns' rugby club. Or some speed racer's brains scattered all over Tawny Hill, his young body ejected from the vehicle after colliding with the otter statue in the centre of the tidy towns' memorial roundabout. They were great for tidy towns in Bally.

It was a place where you went to knuckle down, and follow the rules. Overbearingly polite middle-class white smiles blinded you at every turn. Servile, gutless, sexless. It was a grey, dumb, dreary, piss-ant, nothing of a town.

Its population remained undisturbed by notions of better things, each grimly accepting their lot. For the most part, they just waited around patiently and politely for their own deaths to come and ass-fuck them into the dirt. For the most part.

And the crows, having fuck-all else on, just sat around watching, and bitching, and waiting for the next quiet sadness to unfold.

#

Jack had the Mac pumping.

The lads sang together about stepping into velvet moments. Their voices, mannish and guttural, clambered and jostled roughly in and out of tune. The volume on the radio was loud enough to drown out the roughest edges, so it seemed to them that it was their voices that propped the tinny radio speaker's melody aloft, and even lent to it a subtle consonance that it may otherwise have lacked.

The song ended, and Jack turned off the music so they could assess their progress. An inventory of self was required.

Shane was lying down in the back seat rubbing his hands up and down his torso. He had already stripped down to his vest, and you could tell by the way he tugged at it that he wanted that off too. He was breathing quickly and loudly through his nose and groaning slightly. 'Mmm, hmmm, mmm.'

'What's that, Shaney kid?' asked Jack.

'I was just saying there, them lyrics ya know?'

'Stop. They're insane,' said Jack.

'Oh man, completely, absolutely. Like, fucking mental, like. It's like, some people just know things, and they just understand things, and when they sing them, they can tell us, and that's why everyone loves Fleetwood Mac, because the things they tell us are the truth, and when we hear it we know they're not lying to us, and we love them for that, for telling us the truth like, even if it's a sad truth. Like, it's even more beautiful sometimes, if it's sad you know, because it makes us feel less alone with our own sadness, especially if it's the truth you know, and that's why, man, that's why, eh, that's why, eh…' He took a deep breath. 'Jesus. This shit is fizzing through me now, lads. I'm like a starchy towel, lads, just all wrinkled, too many folds in my fabric.'

'Your folds are grand. You'll be grand,' said Jack, reaching back to pat Shane on the leg.

Shane wriggled in the back, squirming like a dying snake. 'Oh, lads, I'm not sure anymore. It feels a bit fast. Things are going a bit fast. I probably shouldn't have double dropped. There's a degree of kittens drowning in a bucket going on.'

Gerry, who had only moments ago been on the verge of a breakdown, was lying back in his own seat wearing a pair of sunglasses. He reached behind him and clasped Shane's hand. 'Don't worry, man. Let it wash over you. We got you, brother. Just give it a second to level out okay?' Gerry gave his hand a little squeeze. 'I love you, man.' How easy the words came to him. How natural and right they sounded. Why had he never told his friends he loved them before?

Jack smiled, bobbing his head while looking at Gerry. Both of them holding and touching Shane as he shifted about in the back.

'Uuugghhh,' said Shane. 'It's a bit much, lads. Maybe I should sit this one out, lads. Maybe I should go to the hospital. I should probably go to the hospital.'

'Not at all,' said Gerry giving his hand another squeeze. 'You'll be grand in a tick. Jack, throw on another song there for our man. Smooth out those wrinkles for him.'

Jack, took his phone out and started to swipe through his music. 'I got just the thing. Shane kid, you just relax there and I'll sort you out.'

The song came, gentle chimes, soothing synths, and the eerie healing tones of Enya. It was the tune from *Lord of the Rings*. 'This one,' said Jack. 'This one always cheers me up when I feel like killing myself. The essential humanity of it all. The innocence of the hobbits in the face of such corruption is beautiful. Something wholesome about it. This should smooth out your wrinkles nicely.' He kept patting and rubbing with his free hand.

Shane just kept squirming and lifting up his vest, rubbing his hands all over his chest, tweaking his nipples.

Gerry squeezed his hand. 'Jesus, Jack, what's in these things? He's off his game.' Gerry's spoke words of concern, but his voice was all pancakes on a Sunday, and his face was smiling, benevolent, Christ-like behind the dark sunglasses. He felt amazing.

'He's fine, Ger. The skinny lads always feel it a bit more on the way up. He'll smooth out. Just listen to the hobbit music, Shaney, and you'll smooth out just fine. What about you, Ger? How you feeling? You feeling it?'

Gerry paused, then raked a hand through his hair. 'I just hit a wave the very second you asked me that. Fuck man. These are too strong.' He started to rub the top of his head, clenching and unclenching his fist around tufts of hair. 'How are we gonna do it in this state? There's no way.' He was breathing all fast and heavy like Shane was before. 'Oh jeez, now I'm fizzing too. Oh fuck me, Sam really loved Frodo didn't he? And it was such a pure love. Like, it was a love that could only exist in a book. I can see why you would turn to it—oh fucking hell—' Gerry bent over and pressed his forehead against the steering wheel.

'That's it, Gerry, just ride it out. Just a small bit of turbulence while we take off. We'll be at cruising altitude before you know it.'

Gerry looked over to Jack, his cheek still pressed in the clammy rubber of the steering wheel. 'You'd never actually do it though? Would you?'

'What? Top myself? And end up like those poor bastards up there?' Jack nodded to the three crows on the telephone wire.

The trapped souls screamed and screamed and screamed, but all the lads heard was, 'Caw, caw, caw.'

'Ah fuck it, Jack, don't start that shit about the crows again. Not now.'

'Relax, Ger. I'm only winding you. Lookit, this is the hard part. It'll even out soon I promise. Hang on, I have an idea. Wait here.' Jack got out of the car.

Gerry shouted after him in alarm. 'Wait! You can't just leave us here!'

Jack just smiled back. He walked around to the driver's side window, and made the roll-it-down signal with his hand. It took Gerry a minute to figure out the lever, but he eventually managed to get the window rolled down. Jack leaned in. 'I'm just going up the road for a sec. Hang tough, keep an eye on Shane. He probably shouldn't have double dropped. But you and me are okay, aren't we?'

'Yeah. Yeah, you and me are okay, Jack.'

'Good man. Now, gimme them sunglasses. I need them.'

Gerry handed them out the window, and when he took them off Jack laughed at him.

'Jesus, your eyes, man, they look like fucking marbles!'

'Jack, I'll need those back. Don't forget to bring them back.'

Jack winked. 'Trust me, Ger. I got you, man.'

Gerry watched Jack walking off, wondering where the fuck he was off to. Shane moaned in the back seat. The hobbit song was earnestly climbing toward climax. He looked back and could see Shane was crying.

'Shane. Hey, Shane. Talk to me, man. What's happening?'

'I'm fizzing, man. Every inch of me is vibrating with pure potential. We can do anything, like. We're free, Ger. We've always been completely free, we just didn't know it.' Then he tensed, moaning and shivering like a lab monkey.

Gerry clenched his teeth. He craned his neck to get a better look at the crows. Things were becoming intense. The windows were starting to fog. The two lads were panting. Shane finally lost his vest and now wore it over his face.

Gerry, feeling the heat too, kicked off his shoes and peeled his socks off. He felt better as the cool air hit his sweating toes. 'Fucking socks.' He leaned back to talk to Shane. 'Shane, Shane man, it's the socks. Take off your socks you'll feel better. The socks are blocking your circulation, man.'

Shane had his eyes squeezed shut and was humming the hobbit tune, shaking his head back and forth.

Gerry turned around and started to unlace his friend's shoes. 'Don't worry, man. It's the socks. You'll understand once they're off.'

As he pulled at Shane's laces, he could feel the sweat gathering on his brow and stream down his ribs from his pits. He was blinking it from his eyes now, and with each blink was visited by a red flash of images projected onto his eyelids. Images in which he bludgeoned Shane's face in with his own shoes. The drugs were going sideways.

By the time he got to the socks, he was starting to panic. The process had become too involved. The taking off of Shane's shoes seemed to be an obvious allegory, not just for their situation and not just for his life, but for something even vaster than that. It disturbed him that the shoes did not come off easier.

When Ger finally got the socks off, he sat back into his chair as though he had just defused a bomb. He needed very much for things to be okay. He felt his resolve waning. He thought about his son. He thought about the crows. A sadness stirred within him, twisting in his guts like sour milk. He knew that if it were to rise from the depths it would consume him entirely.

And Shane, whose mind was blown wide the fuck open, felt it too. He felt it through the wool and heat of his own inner dealings. Something about the kid, Shane thought. Gerry had a little boy once. He didn't talk about it. Nobody did. Nobody could. Shane sat up. He knew he must speak. So he opened his mouth and forced the words to come.

'You were right. It was the socks.' Shane felt as though he were a dog trying to speak English. All he knew was that his heart was beating too fast, and that Gerry was about to burn himself up. If Gerry was lost then they were both lost. He pinched the bridge of his nose tightly and set to forcing the world right side up again, jamming manners down the gullet of reality. 'Yeah, man, yeah, much better without socks. Phew. Starting to come out of it a bit now,' he lied. 'I think we'll be okay with the socks off.'

Gerry smiled, but it was the smile of a fisherman that had sailed too far out to sea and snagged some terrible doom in his nets. Then grimly, as though its emergence were inevitable, began to reel in his line.

'No need to reel it in, man,' said Shane. 'The socks are off. We'll be grand.'

Gerry knew what he meant. He didn't believe in telepathy, but things were getting to a stage where he felt he could no longer rule out some kind of biological synergy. Thoughts transmitted, not by magic, but maybe via some kind of pheromone in their sweat, some class of hormone exchange. Either way, Gerry knew exactly what Shane was saying to him. The heart of the words were there, beating in the stale air between them. The knowing, and the knowing of the knowing, and that knowing too, and on and on forever, each a mother to a child and a child to a mother. Gerry stopped reeling his nets, and let the great ponderous shadowy nightmare of his past submerge slowly back into the depths from whence it came. 'Yeah, man. It was the socks,' he said.

Shane laughed. 'Yeah, man. Those fucking socks.' And just like that they were safe again.

Gerry looked around, coming out of it a bit.

The windows had fogged up completely now. A narrow shaft of light had broken between a gap in the overhead gloom. It radiated a strange and muted daffodil haze through the window condensation, an eerie end-of-the-world kind of light.

'Can you put that hobbit song back on please?' asked Gerry. He was holding out Jack's phone to Shane, a slight wince pinching his features. The simple task of finding and selecting the hobbit song loomed over him like the threat of violence.

Shane gently took the phone from his friend's hand. 'Good idea,' he said.

Then they sat and listened for a while. It seemed like they might be okay. They were on fire, all popping neurons and electric nerve ends, waves of intensity breaking and receding. It was too much, but it was okay too.

The passenger door opened. It was Jack. He penetrated the delicate atmosphere of the car, brutishly heaving himself into the passenger seat, disturbing the air with his body. 'Jesus H. Christ alive, lads. We definitely should not have double dropped these fuckers! I just had the best fucking talk with the lad at the offie. What a nutter. Some strange heads wandering around out there, lads. But lookit, we can't go in like this, lads. I barely made it out of the offie alive, never mind the fucking bank. We need to calm way the fuck down, like. Smooth out our towel ruffles or whatever, smooth them right out to fuck before we even think about stepping into that bank.'

Jack's presence was jarring. Both Shane and Gerry were sitting forward now, focused intensely on the rabid pulse of chaotic energy that had just landed.

'Surely we're not still going ahead?' said Gerry, his nerves set to jangling all over again.

'Surely we are, my man,' said Jack. 'Now is the perfect time. Can you feel the crackle of the destiny in the air, the hum of fate in your bones? It's like opera music.'

Shane looked at Gerry, and Gerry at looked Shane, and neither could deny it. They were doing it. They were doing it today.

'Don't worry, lads. I got us some corner softeners, a few cheeky towel straighteners.' Jack opened the plastic bag at his feet and pulled out a bottle of Powers and a lash of cans. He broke off a can and passed it over to Gerry, then one back to Shane.

'Ah stop, cans!' said Shane. 'Why didn't I think of that?' Shane cracked the tinny and sucked it down like a halfway insane twenty-eight-year-old man who was tripping too hard in the back of a knackered old Fiesta and about to rob a bank. 'Oh, cans,' he said, kissing the tin. 'Never leave me.'

The very proximity of the booze was reassuring to him. The fact that it was there, warming in the plastic bag between Jack's feet, was enough to steady him. Booze was how you slowed down the squirrels in your head, made them dozy enough to catch, made them placid and pliable. You could, in Shane's experience, drink your way out of any problem. Slow the squirrels, gather them up in your arms, and stroke their fur til they purred with acquiescence and kindness. Booze was a dear, dear friend of his, an unflappable ally in the face of the uncaring void. 'Good man, Jack, you absolute legend of a man.'

Jack cracked his own tinny and cheersed with his friends.

Gerry was smiling too, warmed by Shane's new confidence. 'Fuck it,' he said. 'Cheers, lads. Here's to getting rich.' They sucked on their beers and all involved felt a great deal better.

'Here's to getting the fuck out of Bally!' said Jack. They all cheersed again, the sticky smell of sudsy beer filling the small car.

'We can move on now from the fucking hobbit love song, can we? Something a bit meatier,' said Jack.

'Ah now,' said Shane. 'Nothing too meaty, like. We're only just recovering here for fuck's sake.' He took another long dirty pull from his can. The beer spilled down his chin and pooled in his belly button, but he didn't care. It was giving him his life back.

'Don't worry, kid, nothing too meaty yet, just something to improve our temperaments and overall physicality. Now let me tune the sonic vibrations to eeeeeasy.'

The lads waited expectantly. Their breathing had slowed, and the atmosphere of barely suppressed panic had been diluted by a semblance of calm.

The first loose notes of a playful piano came over the speakers, followed shortly by the lyrics. It was the theme song to *Cheers*.

'You gone done it now, Jackie boy!' said Shane hunching between the two front seats once more. Jack and Shane belted out the first verse and when it came to the part about everybody knowing your name, even Gerry couldn't resist.

The song ended, and the lads held onto one another. Jack put a hand around the neck of each friend and pulled their heads in close so the three of them were pressed together at the forehead. 'This is it, lads. This is fucking it. Today is going to be our day.'

Shane pulled back.

'Shane, kid, take your time.' Jack reached into the plastic bag at his feet and passed another can back to him. The lads weren't ready. Jack knew this. They would never be ready, not like he was ready. But he could fool them into thinking they were. He just needed to stroke them right. They were loose now, dispersed, evaporated from the drugs.

Now all he had to do was put them back together in a manner that best suited the job.

Jack blinked, rubbing his eyes. He was fizzing hard as fuck himself, but he could take it. He loved this shit. They were out in the woods on this one, he knew, way past bedtime. They'd ducked under the do-not-pass yellow police cordon and they were out in fuck-knows-what-now territory.

Jack smiled, because he knew, like all frontiersmen knew, that this is where the magic happens.

'Lads,' said Shane. 'I feel a bit better now. I mean for a while there I didn't feel so hot. For a while there I thought I was gone and not coming back.'

'We got you man, and you got us,' said Jack, taking his shoes off. 'Offt, sorry now, lads, my feet are honking. We'll have to crack a window here.'

'You want me to roll these back ones down?' asked Shane.

'Do, kid,' said Jack.

'Fuck it let's air her out,' said Gerry rolling his window down too. The sharp twang of fresh air gave them each a pang, a stab of lucid pleasure. The air was electricity, energy and life, delicious everything.

Jack reached once more into his bag of tricks and pulled out a box of Marlboro lights. He opened the pack and tossed one over his shoulder and into the back seat without looking. Then he took off Gerry's sun glasses and placed them back on the bridge of his friend's nose. 'They look better on you, Gerry.' He felt Gerry relax as soon as the glasses settled on his face.

He heard a high pitched 'Sweeeet,' from Shane in the back. 'Fire?'

Jack tossed him the lighter. 'I know you're off 'em. Fuck it, we're all off 'em, lads, but today is a special day.'

'No argument here, Jack. Come here you dirty little slut of a fag,' said Shane putting the flame to his cigarette.

Jack fished one out for himself then passed one to Gerry. They were fizzing to fuck, the whole lot of them, but the ruffles and ridges, the edges and snags were rounding down and smoothing out.

Jack flicked through his phone, pressed a tune and Nina Simone began to sing 'Lilac Wine'. They sat and smoked and sucked on their cans, swallowing capfuls of whiskey with the damp November morning breathing in on them.

Several songs passed without a word.

Then Shane said, 'I think I should have the sawn-off.'

And Gerry said, 'I thought we agreed, I was getting the sawn-off and you and Jack would hold the replicas.'

'Yeah, I know, I know,' said Shane. 'It's just that, well, if things get hairy, you know? I don't want anyone getting trigger happy here. Like, no offense lads, but I'm the least likely to use it. I mean, I don't want to hurt anyone in there, I really don't. That's why I should have it. It's safer for everyone. Nothing against ye, lads, but ye have both been known to fly off the handle on occasion. Jack, sure you know that yourself, and Gerry, 'member that time you bottled your man outside Decks.'

Gerry and Jack exchanged a look.

'What if you gotta pop one off just to quiet the place down, are you capable of that?' asked Jack.

Shane sat up. He was cruising now. The jitters had all but evaporated and he was cruising. 'I'm capable of a lot more than you think, Jack.'

Gerry was cruising too now. The glasses were a big help. The shaded screen between his eyes and the world allowed him a measure of detachment. 'I think he's right, Jack. Shane can do it. Let him have the sawn-off.'

Jack's face was blank as he rubbed his chin. 'Alright. You've got the shooter, Shane. Make us proud.' Jack reached under the seat and pulled out the sawn-off shotgun they'd robbed from the Clancy farm. He handed it back to Shane.

Shane tossed his fag and took the gun in his lap. Then he rolled the window back up, and put his vest back on, then his T-shirt, then his hoodie. Shane held the sawn-off lightly, running his hand up and down the length of it, stroking and fondling the cold perfection of its hard rounded surface. He looked at the clock. It was getting time. Shane, cracked the breach and checked both the barrels. He snapped it shut, and leaned forward again. 'It's getting to be about that time,' he said.

'Hmm, getting to be about that time,' agreed Gerry.

Jack opened the glove box and took out the replica handguns. One for Gerry, and one for himself. Then he handed out the masks, Donald Trump for Jack, Kim Jong-un for Gerry and Leo Varadkar for Shane.

The lads bent putting socks and shoes back on feet without hesitation. Had they known what the story was with the pills bubbling in their guts, they might have waited a bit. They might even have called it off, but as things stood they were unaware how badly they had timed their consumption. It was the enteric polymer that coated the SpongeBob pills which delayed the release of chemicals somewhat longer then they had anticipated. The second dose was only now beginning to dissolve. In a few minutes the effects would be apparent.

'Are we nearly right, lads? The time is upon us. How's the heads?' asked Jack.

'Grand,' said Shane.

'No bother,' said Gerry.

'Alright then—'

Without another word, they pulled on their masks and got out of the car.

It was at this point that time began to slow down. Perhaps it was the drugs. Or maybe, like Jack said, it was the insistent hum of destiny vibrating in each of their skulls. Or maybe the moment was just so dense with imminent repercussion that time had no choice but to slow down in order to allow its swollen passage through the narrow band of occupied universe.

The boys slammed each door, the sounds echoing in quick succession, thunk, flump, clunk, and lingered like gunshots in the empty car-park.

They walk three abreast now, cutting through the silence of the town, car park gravel crunching underfoot as they make their way to the bank entrance.

Then, pushing open the double doors wide, the lads float in. Their blood hot and throbbing, the thrum of it filling their ears. Shining and cursed, ready to grab their own lives by the throat.

Parallels | Miracles

The same streets I walked to meet him
I walk to meet a friend.

A week ago she was told
her prized pup from the litter
had died. But it didn't
die, another dog did.
Her dog had always remained alive.
The dead dog was
another.

These streets were not
the same if I wasn't
walking to meet him.

A woman wrote to say
she had seen me in
an elevator with him
all of us going down.
The description fit, but
the dates did not. I had
not been there, the girl
with long hair was
another.

Maybe she had
never been me
and I remained
untouched?

The landmarks paved
over and disappeared. They
took on second lives, or
had none. Some—I never
find them. Others—the bar
where I got a necklace
signed *Ruthless*, where a
man dreamed of trailing
a leaf down my ribs.

Clare Needham

Safe Words

Sean O'Reilly

This is the text of a speech commissioned by Words Ireland and delivered at Bray Literary Festival on September 29th 2018.

They say start with a joke: Why did Jesus die on the cross?

Because he forgot his safety word.

Your safety word can be anything. Duck. Cosmic. Necklace. Whirlpool. Seventeen-thousand. The word is a signal to stop the ritual. It has more authority than yes or no. Saying the word means you do not want anymore. *I have had enough.* Stop the pain. Release me. This is as far as I can go. Beyond the safety word, if it is not submitted to, there lies a region of horror. Caves of ice. Mad ancestral voices.

The real point of the ritual is to bring about the saying of the word. The pronunciation. The entreaty. The command. *Seventeen-thousand. Seventeen-thousand.* The whole point is the moment of submission to the settled word. The cessation. I have desisted. Put down the scourge. The obedience. And afterwards, the silence in the room, the breath of time.

I want to try to talk about writing as a confrontation with the self, not as some kind of expression of the self. Imagination dead, imagine, to use Beckett. I want to try to talk about that self as something which has a cultural history, and how that history may be what some writers have to struggle against, to be allowed a place in, an existence. Or to put it another way, the formal or technical difficulties a writer might face in the composition of a piece of work may be connected to their own psychic limits and to their position within their own culture, their class, race, gender. In order to do this, I am relying solely on my own experience as a writer and teacher—or whatever the best word is for what happens around the long polished table in the writers' workshop, the *Stinging Fly* workshop in particular.

The focus of the workshop is the draft. It is a weird ambiguous quantity, the draft of a story. It can be shy, garrulous, awkward, sentimental, cold, loud, rushed, too believable. It is early. It is before. A prefiguring. Precursive. Time is all it seeks to make, an alternative time. It may not know what it is, or it may know too soon what it wants to pretend to be saying. And it is studded with safe words. Verbs. Adjectives. Dialogue. Which function as limits to the writer's engagement with the material and with herself. The exquisite thing about the draft is that it is where you can see the carnal relationship between form and content.

'I can't write about that, what would my mother think.' This is something you hear a lot in a workshop. Even if it is not said, it is in the eyes. Dread. Denial. The same face you might see on somebody who has been caught red-handed, the instant before they come up with the cover story. Even if the piece of work being considered obviously solicits some deeper exploration of a theme in order to find an ending, especially a sexual theme—the claim is this: but that is not what I intended to write about—*I know how it looks but that is not what I was doing at all.* I only wanted to write a story about a woman who accidentally rubs up against somebody on the Luas. Or since we're in Bray, lets make it the Dart. It is not about desire, it was an accident.

Embarrassment is what each writer risks when they present the draft of a story. The embarrassment not only of making a balls of it but the fear of something else being seen in the material. But as we know the fear is strangely connected to a desire for it—or why would you do it. Embarrassment—the blush—the angry rejection—makes me think about where the writing is coming from and the deeper question of who is writing. Like somebody telling you about the dream they had last night, they are not the person who had the dream. The dreamer is never present. Neither is the writer.

The one who writes is invisible. They never show their face. They are inside, wherever that is. Who—what—is this interior space? Is it just what we call our privacy? When did it begin? Does it change, grow, die? When did this splitting happen, the division into the public and private? I often ask people in the workshop to think about these questions. And I can't expect them to think about it unless I give them something from myself. For me it was in the activity of prayer. That me who used to kneel by my bed at night and try to speak the prayers and beg for my wishes to come true, bargaining with the master for the satisfaction of my wishes. Please make Jimmy O'Hagan let me into his gang. Please let Anne-Marie sit beside me at mass. In the articulation of the prayer, between the words, I could feel the stirring of someone else, someone never seen by anybody else on the street and who was not happy with the status quo. Someone who you had to shut up, crush and bind with the formulae of words. Someone who wasn't allowed to speak in public or there would be trouble, a red face or the back of the paternal hand.

In trying to ask who this is, the one who takes over the chair and actually does the writing, this haranguer in the gut, the manufacturer of carte blanche, it might be interesting to look at the history of what people have thought it was, what was called the poetic self—poetry being a much older form of vocalisation than the mute speech of narrative prose.

It used of course to be known as inspiration, the muse, the divine afflatus. Blake called it, 'the authors in Eternity' and Yeats, 'a clear articulation in the air.' The qualifications of the poetic self, to quote Ted Hughes were: 'that it lived its own life separate from and for the most part hidden from the poet's ordinary personality; that it was not under his control, either in when it came and went or in what it said, and that it was supernatural.' A visitor from outside the human realm. From beyond the last house. Or think of the dubious person from Porlock who came on business to interrupt Coleridge from the trance of writing 'Kubla Khan'—was it even a man, this stranger?

'A clear articulation in the air'—what do we make of that today? Yeats, the die-hard, was probably the last of that type of talk. Most of us nowadays, happy to have found the line, to have heard it on a walk on the beach, would probably recognise it as an auditory hallucination, we would see the source as being in our own unconscious mind—not from an external power—or a vision of a shimmering beautiful woman exhorting us to compose a rallying cry for the dispossessed Gael, a host, an aisling. This desacralisation of the experience of composition, this translation, is one of the great upheavals in human consciousness. Call it the death of god—all the gods—if you will. In their place, we discovered the modern self. The divided modern agony of Freud, the unconscious, the nightly onslaught of the id. The smiling repressive cops on guard at every soft border. Perversions galore. World war.

But just as we were beginning to come to terms with the idea that we are not masters in our own house, that there was another inside us, a beast, a parricide, a rapist toddler, the ground gave way again and we had to face the idea that there was not just one inside us, but a multitude, and in fact there was no inside anyway, that I am in time like light dancing and dappling the surface of water, a fraught hungry incandescence, multiple points of desire on the river of the language. Language is the medium of desire. Consciousness no more than an epiphenomenon of brain activity.

This from David Lodge's novel, *Nice Work,* 1988. (The character Robyn is a young lecturer in English literature.)

> According to Robyn ... there is no such thing as the 'self' on which capitalism and the classic novel are founded ... there is only a subject position in an

> infinite web of discourses—the discourses of power, sex, family, science, religion, poetry, etc. And by the same token, there is no such thing as an author … there is nothing outside the text. There are no origins, there is only production, and we produce our 'selves' in language. Not *'you are what you eat'* but *'you are what you speak'* or, rather *'you are what speaks you'*…

You are what speaks you. (From human to person to self to subject.)

Let's go back to Beckett. In *How It Is*, a radical metaphor for the self, and for writing, he describes a character crawling through the mud. In between his crawling and his gasping, the character speaks what seems to be the story of his life as he hears it spoken by a voice in his head. The question is where this voice comes from, whether it might not be what we generally call the characters own voice, a voice narrating the story of their life.

The character—for want of better word—meets another of his kind, Pim, crawling in the muck. For some reason, they are driven to communicate and devise a kind of semiotic system, signals delivered by one, the tormentor, on the other, the victim by the use of the right hand.

> table of basic stimuli one sing nails in armpit two speak blade in arse three stop thump on skull four louder pestle on kidney
>
> five softer index in anus six bravo clap athwart arse

Then after a lot of this mutual abuse they get to the writing. One scratches questions in the others back demanding to be told something about their life 'above in the light'. The other obliges with answers. Story. The attempted suicide of his wife for example. Anything. It doesn't matter what. All you have to do is answer.

I, the treasured first person, is what is forced on us. All those who use the first person are victims. To be tortured is the precondition for being humanised. Monologue is an expression of self-alienation, not self-expression. We make stuff up to please the tormentor who demands we speak. The victim, like all victims do, crawls away until it finds another whom it in turn will torture into articulation.

So where is there to go from this as a writer? To write is to fail of course because what you have to say you are being forced to say and it may have no bearing on anything anyway, on some place up there in the light. Learn the prayers and say them. And hope that the next prayer will be the last. But yet you cannot stop, you keep going back to it, reaching that safe word, and starting all over again.

Let's try to look it another way. Eavan Boland in her book *Object Lessons* meditates on the struggle to find a poetic voice for herself in a male national tradition of poetry. In a key chapter, she remembers how she tried to make a poem out of the experience of a conversation with her older neighbour out the front of her suburban house one summer evening.

'As we talk,'—she tells us—'I feel the shadow of some other meaning across our conversation, which is otherwise entirely about surface things. That it is high summer in my life, not in hers. That hers is the life mine will become, while mine is the life she has lost.'

She begins to make notes for a poem about this encounter, aware of that 'half-in-half perspective which is so connected with the act of writing'. She can smell the sweet cut grass, hear her children breathing in their sleep, see the suburban poplars, the shadow of the Dublin hills. But as she sits writing, she knows with complete certainty the poem will never be written.

What went wrong, why did it not feel possible? What was it about the ingredients of that moment, the suburb, the hills, the grass, the last light, two women talking, that could not add up to the texture of a poem? Reflecting back on it, Boland suggests that the failure to write the poem has something to do with what she calls the 'devalued subject matter' of her own experience, two women talking in the suburbs, that somehow this didn't feel like the right theatre for a poem. 'It has given me insight'—she writes—'into the flawed permissions which surround the inherited Irish poem'. The poet finds herself trying to write in a tradition which does not recognise her, which inherently resists her own lived experience, her time.

Boland, however, sees this as a challenge. It is not exactly the background of the poem which is the problem, the setting as we used to call it in school, it was the surface of the poem, the two women talking, the image within the image, the body of one woman being the prophecy of the body of the other. Boland feels she could make neither herself real or the other woman: 'I cannot make the time we are happening in real, so that the time I fear can happen.'

The permission to allow the time I fear to happen.

Rather than struggling with any postmodernist definition of self, Boland here is talking about the confrontation with history, with a tradition. The inner workings of the poem, the technical heart, can work to rebuff and to disenfranchise different perspectives. The form, created over time, wants to protect itself from outsiders and yet of course depends on those outsiders to stay alive, to be in time. This particular gender resistance might be broadened out to similar feelings felt by those from another class or race trying to work within a form which has not yet felt the pressure of their vision. Nowadays we might also add the poetic mainstream's resistance to the spoken word performers.

Form as a receptacle of the dreams of self. Dreams of coherence and meaning and order.

What I'm trying to say here is that many of the problems encountered by writers in workshop are down to the quality of their own introspection and how they find a way or not to connect this self—the creature of their introspection—to the form and style they are trying to use. I think it would be fair to say that most of the writers in the *Stinging Fly* workshops are working in the tradition of realism, and more particularly, the lyrical realist short story which still seems to be the de facto approach to discovery in this country.

The ingredients of this form—character development, dialogue, scene, exposition, plot itself—were developed in another century, with a completely different philosophical and ideological view on the self and reality. Students often seem surprised to realise that they are dealing in something called realism, that there is a name for it, that it is possible to see things differently. Some students are relieved that it has a name which liberates them to question it.

Story is not free of the desire to devalue certain people's experience, as Eavan Boland unearthed about the Irish poem—and to push a bit deeper than that, story contains implicit assumptions about the world, which may no longer be satisfactory for the contemporary writer.

Take just one example. In a 2015 book called *The Good Story*, a written exchange between J.M. Coetzee and the psychoanalyst Arabella Kurtz, Coetzee, after a discussion of the ultimate detective story, Oedipus Rex, remarks that when we read detective stories we are gripped by the characters attempts to preserve the secret. We root for them. We don't want them to find out. Because we cherish the hope of escaping from the past and remaking our life.

'Now'—he writes—'imagine a story that tries to teach exactly the opposite moral: that our lives are ours to make and remake as we wish, that the past is the past, that secrets can freely be buried and forgotten. Can there be such a story that works as a story? Can we have a story that ends, "And his secret was forgotten, and he lived happily ever after"?'

I can't think of one, a good one anyway. And the reason is a dream of justice, an ethical sense—a hope—buried in the very architecture of story, that bad things are punished and good things rewarded, the truth will out, and a rational equilibrium will prevail.

Do you really believe that? Did they really used to believe that in the past?

A change in the instrument of discovery will change what is discovered. A change of style is a change of subject. The observation of a thing alters that thing. How then can this reality supposedly lying beyond all attempts to see it, ever be seen? Art is no longer the mirror held up to nature, the eye is not a recording camera, a medium of witness but the sewer of the soul, to use George Bataille's term.

Our ways of seeing are influenced by ideology as Žižek showed in *A Pervert's Guide to Cinema*. The cinema, he argues, doesn't give you what you want, it shows you how to want. Think of *King Kong*—all that has to happen before the girl and boy can get together, all that must be killed, controlled, before they can form a normalised unit, male and female, drained of desire, ready to produce the family, the next lot. Literature is not somehow above the taint of ideology and its compulsive repetition of the same narratives, the same resolutions, the same safe words. The same sentimental perversions.

Perversion, defined by Adam Phillips, is the opposite of desire, 'an anxious narrowing of the mind when it comes to pleasure'. The pervert is one who constructs a scenario, an obsessively repeated sexual ritual, with the aim of achieving the same outcome, the climax in a safe word. The pervert seeks to keep themselves safe from the risk of hot, uncontrolled desire. The pervert kills sex with sex. They return again and again to the same scenario, the same words, the same gestures, the same cold end.

For Žižek, the scenarios and plots of cinema make perverts of us all. We are trained to need those stories to reassure us, to keep us from harm. We forget the artifice, we forget the camera, the money behind it all, the agenda, and by forgetting, find ourselves addicted. The same might be said of the conventions of literary realism. What might we do with our lady friend on the Dart who accidentally rubs up against people in the rush hour? What does the shape of story demand will happen to her? Will she want to do it again and again? Will she get away with it? How will she be stopped? Whose life will she change—improve—save—by her frottage? What sequence of cause and effect will the sentimentally-perverted writer follow, how can they short circuit the expectations of a reader who is similarly perverted by having read too much literary realism?

Look at what happened to Madame Bovary.

In the workshop I try to remind people that every form carries with it a template for viewing the world, oppressive or optimistic depending on your outlook, class, and these days, your general state of discomfort in your own skin. Literary realism is a kind of fetish in this country. It may not serve the nascent vision of every writer. The almost automatic recourse to particular style of writing may be what lies behind a writers struggle with say, dialogue, or endings, with language itself—the form may be inhibiting the original source of the voice, a voice which quickly gives up, recedes, and leaves the eerie sense of a dim drafty place where time has stopped and people are going through the motions. The writer becomes a reluctant pervert, a pessimistic fetishist, repeating a style that they do not really believe in. The writer is in danger of killing the writing with writing.

Do you really believe in what you're saying here? That is the question I keep asking, in different ways. Go back and think about who is doing the writing and dare to know what they want to say. Be careful that what you are writing is not a disguise, a conventional camouflage, a safety barrier against the writer sensing for example—the utter fictionality of themselves and everyone around them or hitting on the words of a prayer-spell which might awaken the monster of their own futile perjury.

One way I have found to encourage this self-consciousness about form is to keep reminding the writer about the usefulness of other genres for the development of their work. Realism is itself just another genre, a genre based on a lot of dubious and outdated scientific tenets around observation and causality. It barely needs to be said now that there is a crisis in the belief in realism's ability to capture reality anymore, a crisis that has seen a rage for genre-mixing and the dissolution of the line between fiction and non-fiction, autobiography and plot. Just think of Karl Ove Knausgård's five book epic, *My Struggle*.

Or take for example the horror genre where there are some very exciting and wonderful things going on. Eugene Thacker's *Horror of Philosophy* trilogy takes up the position that the intuitions of horror writing are the best philosophy available to us in the current times. The first book, *In the Dust of This Planet*, was the inspiration behind the television series *True Detective*. Thacker's trilogy is part of a modern brand of philosophical pessimism, speculative realism it is generally called, which in rejecting much of what traditional science tells us about the world, and our consoling myths for the future, tries instead to build a realism that does not promote a sense of the total intelligibility of the world, a moral world with humans at its centre, and instead reaches for an uncanny realm which may lie just beyond our senses, beyond what we can even dare to think, beyond the horror of thought itself.

Writing is a ritual enacted in a space that once was considered sacred, a place the gods might visit. We write in the ruins of the centuries. We crawl through the dust and the muck, the wires, shouting safe words that no longer work, inflicting torture on whoever we encounter, to make them talk, just as we were made to talk. Beckett saw no end to the crawling—there was no hope of Godot or the man from Porlock to come knocking to interrupt the trance flow, as Coleridge claimed when writing 'Kubla Khan' and his sunny pleasure dome with caves of ice. Maybe it was a lie and there was no interruption. Maybe he just couldn't finish it. Maybe he was too afraid to finish it. Maybe it was a visitor from the future-time.

Nevertheless the poet Stevie Smith longs for a visit from someone from Porlock.

I long for the Person from Porlock
To bring my thoughts to an end,
I am becoming impatient to see him
I think of him as a friend...

I am hungry to be interrupted
For ever and ever amen
O Person from Porlock come quickly
And bring my thoughts to an end.

we have forgotten

a response to 'Dapunta Hyang: Transmission of Knowledge' by Zai Kuning

how to love the taste of careless freedom
the sweet hollow of buoyant ribs that carry us
along unchartered coasts our endless home
there was a time
when
people had gills instead
of lungs & breathing did not matter
there was a time
when we would scrap the scales off
each other's limbs every February
in time
for the monsoon to wash us dry
do you
remember
the boats we carved from
the husk of our sun-dried bodies?
gnarled fingers fastened each bone
upon weathered bone
with crimson wax binding all futures
to every known past
it is said that once you drink
from briny lips you must never
look back
there are columns of salt
beached on the shore
to prove it I was told

that once the plaintive shoreline
turns into a bed of green moss it is time
for us to exchange the ropes of
our freedom for the anchor of dry land
I remember waking up one night to find broken
fingers
sewn to my hands & I had forgotten
how to serenade my lonesome lover the sea
I could not
tell the names
of each island or the faces
of each stone
my gills had left me breathless & there I stood
naked & rooted
to a guilty coast

Esther Vincent Xueming

Triangle

Oisín Fagan

1. It could have been a passionate love triangle, but he was always on his phone and I could never remember what colour her eyes were. She mistook everything for aging; teeth becoming transparent, grimacing in sunlight, a growing attachment to silence, coughing in the morning. There was not enough compression in their lives, and she wanted me to pay more attention to the signs, of which there were none. At night, in winter, her blood runs hot and she fidgets, anxious to have sex with someone who doesn't have my smile. I see her first in a supermarket, lengthening a queue; narratives emerge and unravel in her face over the course of a shopping list. Her sighs are medieval and she looked different in every photo, but only from herself. She reminds me of dying, perhaps, but I don't remember why. An age of sentimentality has eclipsed her friends and in its shade they create new concepts with which they attempt to justify their dislike for me. At the time I was dreaming of bright days, unemployment benefit and pussy so hot it would blister our fingertips. In the beginning she was allergic to her lover. Wherever he breathed, sores would emerge. Eventually the inside of her thighs looked like the craters of the moon. I wanted her a little less every time, but I still wanted her. Sooner or later we all get used to it, and she becomes inoculated against me, so it is time for him to leave

in an inglorious kind of hand-me-down fashion. Often, when I am in storage, when I am stored, I pretend the other boxes contain monsters. This is the difference between you and me.

1. Made lonely by forces within her control, he is a centrifugal force which repels generosity, and she did not want to make the effort to be misunderstood. I spin away, forgetting. In her phone was his number and I could tell by the digits and the flat functionality of his one-syllabled name that too many opinions had closed him up. I call giddy children little bitches to their faces in order to regret it later, and sit at the edge of public fountains taking pictures of pigeons with her in the background, a blur on the edge of her own life. I can convince them to do anything. Frigidity and stasis were aspirations they slipped into, and since they had nothing good to spend their money on I had no guilt whatsoever when I spent it on tracksuits. I was always forgetting the things she didn't do anymore. She lacks the necessary tragic moments off which to hang the loneliness of her nights. There is a certain boredom to his dreams and fears, which allowed them to bumble their way into marriage, a deeper pastiche of emotion, with the cruel and calm inevitability of a focussed child who destroys garden furniture at family barbeques. Their dreams were borrowed, but the pain was real.

2. You, I suspect, wake up in the night, eyes full of tears, missing your family because you are an uncaring son. I spend her mornings by the windowsill, thinking up excuses to continue wasting his time. It is enjoyable to become the cliché projected onto me. He once fell asleep on my shoulder during sex, which has made him fall in love with me. I have no potential anymore, not even his. You were the worst summer of my life, and everybody knows it. You don't even want me, you just want children who look like me. Memories used to intoxicate me, but now everything is softer to the touch. Still, one day I will think of having memories fondly. Very occasional invitations

seem incessant, and the mornings are quiet. My face is formless, but so is yours. Every time I close my eyes a fresh sensation buckles under my skin, sending a message out across the planet that you should open your eyes in the next room. After a certain point, life becomes similar to itself. Death becomes an indifferent prospect, like a forthcoming meeting with a distant relative at lunchtime. Too many headaches have taken the joy out of doing nothing, the little anxieties covered in festivals that invented the calendar, so I get a job. This is my final failure. You are about to witness the first victimless suicide. Not my own, of course, just the sanctity of my private life, which I used to call ambition.

1. I will never remember our first night together. On our second one, though, shadows fucked against the wall while we were asleep on our backs, not touching each other. Cold nose in the morning, a square of light on the wall, a shadow that nothing projects. These are the moments which tie together the message you never communicated. She shifted her failures off herself by blaming me, but some night responsibility must start and I won't be in the building on the day that it all ends. I have a childish infatuation with large breasts, and she has a childish infatuation with being understood. The evenings were too long and dark to have no vices so she addicted me to hope; still, she was disappointed before I even took my clothes off. Many lives have a certain density that you can unravel in passing.

1. If I were ever to think of him, which I don't, I would imagine he wanted to be obsessive, but was worried I would find his fixation unattractive so, inevitably, like cancer patients, we gravitate towards the gentle stability of hobbies. He had something to prove, but no one to tell. Our mornings together drained away like blood from a bag. Occasionally, I meet violent people and they are kind to me, sensing my neutrality in the face of life. The one time I saw him was in a social space full of self-impressed people making histrionic attempts to intensify their mediocrity by blaming it on me, because

I am so beautiful and so frigid. There was a time, twenty years ago, he tells me, when being slightly retarded and giggling too much was attractive. We all miss those irredeemable days. She never belonged to me, but he did. I shocked him into a deeper lethargy than the one he had previously inculcated. He spent his whole life seeking women's validation and then failed to recognise it on the one occasion I granted it to him. I gave him his only moments of life. My jealousy, which was beautiful, could have animated a certain, similar beauty in his features, if he hadn't withheld the toll you must pay to lose something. I was the master of his sadness, but I never used it and she was never given the chance to reject me.

1. She had a cat called Franco. I once got her menstrual blood in my eye. The sun goes left and up. We had nothing to give. I forgot his name, so I give him my own. There are not enough of them to go round, in any case. I accumulate too many of the things given to me by bemused bystanders as the years go by. I must reuse these special, chosen names on newer lovers, which is the only betrayal for which I have ever felt any guilt. You are surpassed, not by time, but by the completion of documentation. The days are distinct, self-contained units, tied together by dietary habits. We immolate them with naps and when I wake up I remember the little moments of your face, and am always hungry and lonely, and the light is different and I am afraid. My life is full, like an overflowing dustbin. This love triangle has only one side. I was never fallen in love with.

3. She thought it was uncouth to laugh at people, and she read books on evolutionary biology, nodding her head too much. I play FIFA in the evenings next to my ashtray, finding solace in the weatherman's more apocalyptic prognostications. I was too simple and loving for her, but also for me. When you start a relationship young the accident is written into the fabric of your life until you are a pervert, but if you don't, you have not given yourself up with proper abandon to comfort. Under my dream of swimming in oceans of pussy there is no

consciousness, just an empty space we don't venture into anymore. There is nothing underneath these manners. I left my protective clothing in a drawer from my childhood and have been vulnerable ever since the map ran out of battery. She thinks she is unique, but I hate most people, too; I'm just too polite to say anything. He, on the other hand, like everyone, is enjoying the anonymity of my life. I thought I was the special one, but I have no way to show it. I will not think about her anymore. My opinion, or, perhaps, my closing argument, is that we are all unequal, and that I am the least.

1. Too much sex, like any other pastime, led to the stale discharge of timetabled perversity. When people talked to each other about fucking, glasses in hand, in smart clothes, after work, I had no idea what they were discussing. We are from a small nation so we are not private, we are resentful, which is, of course, a good thing. She is European, but not in the way she wanted to be. If Europe existed it meant fountains, stone buildings and other asinine totenkopfs. I do not build my empire around these things. She was stoned, busy, lazy on the weekends. The only truth that could destroy her would be the discovery I have made, and then hid, that she is almost boring. We are under the pillow somewhere. Items lose character, and the new is another category of loss. My face, unpainted, is architecture for the soul. Haemorrhoids appeared on his cheeks after the first year, scales on the soles of her feet the second, fish hooks for teeth when I die. My favourite word is disperse. Nothing is vital. The money he earned was mine. What was special about him was that there was so little of him that nothing was missing. She dreams of conversations where she can call things decadent, romantic, gilded, sumptuous, exquisite, but I never speak with my mouth full.

2. We can't all be incandescent. Near the end, to make it the end, I put a lot of effort into fucking him, tantalising him with fake symbols. Painted nails, frills, razors, eyeliner, wiry hair, a kitten voice. I begged him to shower less often, not to wear shirts, deodorant or condoms, but he

was a coward, and he used passing windows as mirrors too often for me to respect him. My lovers have all been puny and idiotic. I only half deserve them. If you take away jealousy, the greatest part of love is gone; and he is not jealous enough. I was the only one amongst the three of us who was jealous enough to merit fidelity. He looked more like a caricature of a man than he looked like a man. Sometimes I feel I am just one fuck away from happiness, but, of course, I always get a headache when I am happy. I would have liked one real lover who could dominate me on occasion, but, who, for the most part, was my bitch. Men are forever trying to get me pregnant just so they can fuck me in the third trimester. I wrap my legs around their backs when they start crying. I am a pair of jaws, a few eyes in a head, a feverous morning; my best quality is that I am unlikeable. Sensitive people, idiots, believe their passions to be rationality and mine to be cruelty, but jealousy has its rights, too, no? It has more rights due to it than your weakness does, despite your limp insistence. I would become a lesbian if women weren't so boring and unattractive.

2. This longing is merciless. It is for no one, so it will never stop. Snow falling has the sound of rain making love, or perhaps of buried rain; I haven't decided which yet, and there is no compulsion to decide. My own self, and the identity you attempt to thrust upon me, is a small compartment of a consciousness which is driven by pleasure, whereas your flailing self is driven by a wounded ego, which I have been obliged to call pain ever since you, armed with only your jarring sincerity and a spoon, ambushed me over dinner. The only thing more embarrassing than my hedonism is your moralism. I have always hated you since yesterday.

3. Her nightmares were monumental, historic schisms of the planet. Everything collides, and still nothing happens. I looked at her body, happy. I always want one moment less. It was then she was most inhuman, which I loved. I never remember her dreams. There is always some part of her left to fuck. Still, I would have liked to

have spoken to him, one man to another, about how much we didn't understand each other, but I could already foresee my desperation, his detachment, the swallowed sigh of her eavesdropping.

3. The only thing greater than my jealousy is my fear of losing you. I feel sick every time I think of the sex you had with other people. I used to go crazy because you weren't a virgin. There is something unforgivable in the fact that you weren't faithful to me before you met me; once you had met me, of course, I could understand then. You should have known you were mine since you were a child. There is a room in which his cock is being sucked. Everything drips out of my sex, constellations, blood, dreams, solitude, the future, romance, often nothing. Something else limps to the bathroom. He looks nothing like my mother, and I am in front of a computer screen, pretending I am able to sleep without you next to me. The truth is I am afraid of losing you, and the slightest request on my part will make you leave me. I refuse to live without you; I did that for twenty years, and I was not enough to manage it. You will leave me soon, though, and when you do my only victory will be that I was irreproachable. You can say this makes me weak, risible, hateful, but I would rather you saw me as something detestable than didn't see me. I will never show you all these emotions you have conjured up in me, even at the single crucial moment that faces us all when we are alone in front of the one person we love. You only give me a headache, you just gift wrap it in lace.

2. The only way left to meet new people nowadays is to sleep with them. New rooms welcome you, messy and silent, unseen until dawn when everything is dizzy and I blur. A car passes by and I wish I was in it, being abducted by aliens, outlaws or, at the very least, family. In the earlier, more raucous days of dating sites terrible things happen. It slowly emerges I have slept with a man who dresses up as animated characters and goes to conventions on the weekends, an arts student who wants me to help him with his assignment, a

man at least fifteen years younger or older than his profile suggests. I wanted something debonair and all I got was a certain frictionless side effect. Without projects, I drift towards the icy chill of cocaine, waiting for my twenties to end. An entire evening spent looking at the graffiti in a bathroom stall, waiting for you to finish speaking. I destroy friendships of ten years for a moment's privacy. Guilt gives everything the warm shimmering tones of childhood. The only person who ever fascinated me is bald, a hundred and thirty kilos, Gargantuan, working class, the only man under forty I knew could wear a moustache without looking like a faggot; he ate the strangest food, the spinal fluid of tuna, the brains of sheep, the tongues of lizards, sucked joints like there is no time left, and fucked me like I wasn't even in the building. He got into fights, and cried like a child watching films about Italian teenagers who fall in love. I don't need sex, he would say to me, I only get head; which, to me, still seems extravagantly romantic. We are on a terrace overlooking the sea. Obviously, he doesn't exist, but he must have been somewhere once.

2. That was the first time I saw you, my husband always says, because he hasn't seen me since. I am unpicked by fingers. The greatest part of me is hidden, so don't look under the covers. My life is a wreck. This iceberg is showing the most of itself. Being with you is like being alone, being with him is like being with too many people.

1. We were always disintegrating. I like her belly and her breasts, and I cheated on her twice and left in the process of her finding out. Hurt is a shorthand she writes because she doesn't have the time to make me exquisite. The women I've disappointed only know what you don't tell them. My ideas are for sale, and her identity is an illusion borne of his fear of being alone. It took me two months to forget I ever happened to them. I am forever reading horror stories to myself about her, aloud.

The Coat

worn dusty dark donkey jacket with leather patches on the shoulders hanging on a
rack outside a
shop with. a forecourt
other objects are placed around
pieces of. junk
including a table bearing some chipped china plates and some tarnished brass
trinkets
there are two salesmen
one who is in the shop is the Son of an older man who is out the back
the. Son is thin has fine blonde hair and is wearing a red check shirt
the father is shorter and wears a beige overcoat with. wide lapels it is double breasted
and has a
belt
he stands with his hands in the pockets
his face is drawn in at the cheeks and he has short light brown hair
blue eyes
he has. a frail ascetic bearing
the Coat has no price on it
it is very dirty and needs to be cleaned and repairs done to its various holes
i ask how much the Coat costs and i am told. four pounds
this is too much and i will pay no more than two
i say to the Son no i shake my head.
the Father is in the background
the Son looks to him and he looks to me
i signal with my outstretched arm. and two raised fingers that two pounds is the price
i want
he comes towards me and i go towards him

there are some other old gentlemen with him
we are in an open space it's like a back yard
the other gentlemen. are wearing dark suits and smoking cigarettes
the Son joins the Father
he is not sure that the Coat is worth more. than two pounds
and he stands in an attitude of non-committal to either party
i hold the Coat up to the Father
pointing out to him its drab condition and the fact that it needs to be cleaned
four pounds. for this i say
look at it it is filthy dirty
it will cost me four pounds to have it cleaned
the material is worn out and look it has a hole in the back
it's only worth two pounds i'll. give you two pounds for it my argument is forceful
and the Father is won over
at this point though one of the older gentlemen
who has been talking about other business with the Father says to him
I'll give you four pounds for it
it is obvious that he. doesn't want the Coat and i look at him in surprise he looks back
from below his
brows and says just. to stop a catholic having it

Kieron Corrigan

Loosely defined it was a relationship

Hilary White

Within which, if I were to put myself, here or now. I'm not. We radiate around the outsides.

I started to question, quite regularly, the way I was relating to all things.

I play a language-game. I am playing two games with language that are related to one another but not in the way you would expect. What is the relationship between two things that function solely by their relationship to one another. It is not. And yet you still think you can be inside and outside, that the relationships within bear relation to those without. I propose we look carefully at this, maybe forever, until we've figured something out.

At some point I was playing a game where I submerged myself in a system only to sink right through. I became dismantled, or something did. The question was how to look at a relation. The question was sinking right through.

*

In New York I was so tired all the time. The weather turned quickly over three days, from being too hot to carry my suitcase up the steps to Pulaski Bridge to a gloomy seventeen degrees. On our last night I alienated a YouTube sensation. He talked about making YouTube videos like it was a real thing to do. He was from upstate New York.

I left at 6.30 in the morning to a beautiful pink sunrise, talking to the taxi driver about how neither of us could sleep. We were silent for long periods. He lived near the airport so I was his last trip that night, that morning.

Austin looked so dry compared to everywhere else I knew. I struggled with road crossings and couldn't figure out how to get the bus to stop. Groceries were expensive and my small kitchen unit didn't even have cutlery. I bought a knife and ate only food I could slice. I was still very tired in Austin. A week or more of jetlag. I thought everyone was my enemy. Or perceived me as theirs. I ate alone in restaurants and was silent for whole evenings. When I was less tired I would spend them reading.

*

The first week went slowly. After that I didn't notice the time passing, or it passed so quickly that I couldn't note it. I spoke to friends on Sundays. Usually while visiting the launderette. If I was speaking to somebody they would remark on the sounds, and I would tell them it was the birds screaming in the trees just outside. I didn't know the type (the trees or the birds), but later learned the birds were grackles. I started to enjoy myself immensely.

During that first week, a new bug appeared in my room each day. I either killed or removed them, based on a snap judgment as to their deadliness. Then I tracked them down on the internet to find out what they were. (I did love to learn new things.) One night I shared my room with a mosquito and woke up covered in red lumps. The next evening I smashed the mosquito on the back of my hand. It left a red stain on my palm. I wondered if the blood was all mine. I got used to the smell of bug spray before bed, the feeling of inhaling it and the taste. Made all the worse because my windows were closed, to keep out the bugs. One Sunday a man drove us to Lockhart, to eat barbeque. He paid for everything. I was a vegetarian, but tried the meat anyway. The whole place smelled of smoke. Greg kept quietly putting pieces of meat onto my plate, I think because he didn't know what to say. The buildings looked so old but I didn't know what that meant here, and there were few people out walking. The blue of the sky, nearly every day in Texas. Usually a piercing mid-blue, like highlighter ink. But that day it was so hot it was cobalt. And cloudless.

I called my friend from the bus stop on the way home. He started telling me that if somebody had a fear of commitment it meant they weren't interested. I wasn't sure how we had gotten onto the topic. He referred to it as a 'home truth'. I wondered if he thought that's what I'd been doing.

I would think about this friend at night sometimes, to the point where I would dream of him. And obviously dreams always feel unbidden. And somewhere in the dream the image mixed with wanting. Wondering whether I had long been ignoring real wanting, or had fashioned wanting out of thinking, out of a space to fill which I filled with thinking. And later, wanting. Night by night, a slow acclimatisation to an idea.

One night I dreamt I was pregnant. I wondered if it was because I was away. In the dream were all my past thoughts about the subject, which is why it felt so real. I went into the dream pregnancy thinking about whether I could keep it, and somewhere developed a new thought that I had not had in real life. That it might be my only chance to have a child. In the dream I planned to keep it. I remember it feeling very much my own body, but when I think about it now it feels so distant. My dreams were often about closeness, but never like this. Perhaps because I'd been spending time with a mother. But was I really that impressionable. All the things I was supposedly lacking, now coming at me in my sleep.

I decided I would have to draw every day, which resulted in my drawing one day. But what was it I was drawing. Loosely defined it was a relationship.

I sent an email to this friend and his scattered response made me hate him for a second. I concluded that my feelings were solely reactions to his actions. All this was was framework, the substance emptied out. Later, I conceded that this empty framework could be a defence, the hate-reaction a way of never getting to rejection. There was no way of knowing that everything else wasn't also like this.

I went from explaining postmodern rootlessness in the German biergarten on campus to explaining that I wasn't homesick because I had laid no foundations. At the time I didn't realise the relation. At this point I was perhaps stuck on the concept of relationality. (The whole world seemed subsumed.) That was the night I came home and squashed the cockroach in my bathroom with a boot.

We were out and I decided I wanted to see all the rooftop bars. We made it to two. Men spoke to us. One of them managed a bakery and dog groomers'. The bakery was, in fact, for dogs. He said: 'bad things don't happen in Austin.' It was the night of the shooting in San Antonio. There seemed to be a new shooting every week. When everybody else left the bar, he said: 'it's so hard being a guy.' He kept showing us the same picture of the themed Halloween cookies for dogs.

One night when I couldn't sleep I heard the plastic on the bin crackling, in a way that was different to the crackling caused by the ceiling fan. I turned on the light and saw in silhouette the cockroach crawling over the edge of the bin. It curled around the lip and was in. I put on pants and closed the bin bag, folding it down around the roach, took it outside to dispose of it. It was like smacking into a wall, the heat when I came back into the room.

The cockroaches had started to come in, and it was time to go. I would be on edge for days at a time without knowing why. I found that if I expected them constantly, they would stop appearing. For a time. I routinely checked the room whenever I came home in the evening. The stillness had broken and the temperature was erratic. Every so often there would be a warm night. There were so few people on the street, and I walked everywhere. I stopped wanting to spend time at home, so every Sunday when I didn't see anyone I would go to this quiet bar and have a glass of white wine. One night a woman yelled at a group for smoking on the patio, and then joined their group to talk. I put some falafel in the microwave and they burned a hole in the plastic container. The room smelled very strongly of burning plastic and I was due to leave the next day.

Back home, I had seen a counsellor about disconnectedness. For her it was a refusal to connect. She said I was making excuses, like a child. She refused to see the pattern I laid out in front of her. The problem, I now knew, was that I didn't ask enough questions. Or was forever asking the wrong ones. There are gaps, you see, she did not take seriously. These gaps, I've found, are difficult to understand.

Every so often someone would leave and the landscape would shift slightly. They would feel briefly disappointed, then fold back into their lives. Already before they left invariably a part of them had started leaving.

I lived every day thinking some terrible event was imminent. It was always about the relation of one person or people to another person or people. I would walk down the street and suddenly be expecting bad news, unable to shake it. Sometimes I just enjoyed the walking.

Sooner or later, something was going to have to happen. But there was something in that, not wanting a story.

Generally, people left me alone. Generally, I preferred it that way.

*

I moved to a new place and within a day there was an infestation of fly larvae. Tiny white worms that seemed to appear from nowhere, even though whenever my eye caught them they weren't moving very quickly. I squashed them one by one, then curiously lifted a rug to find maybe twenty, thirty more. And more again under another rug. I probably killed over a hundred larvae that morning, one at a time. My hosts came to remove the rugs and put them out in the sunlight. The morning had been so peaceful, just reading on the porch. After applying repellent four or five wasps appeared immediately, I couldn't get them to leave me alone. One clung to the book I had clearly coated with the stuff. Towards the end of the summer, or I guess November in Texas, wasps are attracted by sweet smells. It was the only causation I could create. I skyped with my friend who said he was going on a date. It appeared I was very attractive to insects. I washed off the repellent and went out for the evening with bare legs.

Rocky, like the movie, was sitting in a coffee shop patio, calling, one after the other, people he did not seem to know. He kept introducing himself, then explaining his connection to them. One of the recipients of a call was the daughter of someone he'd dated in the eighties. She was at a party so she couldn't talk. He said enjoy the party and hung up.

I wanted to write an essay about archives and bodies, because it had struck me, in reading boxes of letters each day, how many of them were about illness. People wrote when they were ill, when their relatives were ill. I swear there wasn't a single letter in which nobody was ill. As I read letters from the later years, as the archive aged, more and more people started to die. There were so many lives in these boxes and I moved through them so quickly, it became overwhelming, the accumulation of bad news. One week I got a stye, and I emailed a bunch of friends to tell them. I didn't tell my Mom because I thought it would worry her. She was emailing me about my Dad's dialysis procedures. I was reading the papers of an author who said she was dying of kidney dysfunction for at least ten years. I walked around my apartment staring at the floor, expecting to see parts of it wriggling.

I wanted to be so alone that my language would change, and then it did, and all I wanted was to go back.

There were these bare moments everywhere I went.

I worried I was drifting away from some people. But I understood because I was drifting away from me too.

On a bus ride home a woman sat near the front aiming and firing an imaginary shotgun. The whole twenty minutes I was on the bus, she kept lining it up and shooting. Occasionally she made the accompanying noises, sometimes speaking to her target. Bang bang you're all dead. But mostly it seemed like just one target.

I liked it here because there was space between the buildings. You could walk up and down a strip but the places you could go into were spread out. Because I only went to these strips there were not many continuous times indoors.

I was not drawing anything and this was increasingly a problem. I wondered if in only writing about drawing I would forget how to see. If my language would change.

Two weeks after the larvae the flies started to appear. I had been writing about flies in novels. This was all the material I used to make new friends. Kafka mentioned flies in his diaries around then too. We were all of a nervous disposition. I found five dead flies by the window and could still hear buzzing. Later when I turned off the light the buzzing grew in volume. When I turned to look, five live flies. They seemed to come in fives. I doused myself in bug spray and got completely under the covers. It seemed I might suffocate from the fumes. The next day I told the story to a group. 'I had some flies,' I explained to the man. 'Oh,' he said, nodding.

At some point it became home, but I don't know when. At some point you stop paying attention. By the time I was leaving I felt like letting people in. Perhaps I had been preparing for something.

The last few days went quickly. I bought a coffee for a man whose face was covered in blood, standing outside a Starbucks, afterwards wondering if I should have sought medical attention instead. But he was standing there bloodied, arms across his chest, asking for coffee and a hot breakfast sandwich. I wanted to help but wasn't thinking. I left him standing there, still asking for a sandwich. Further down I crossed the street to avoid a wedding.

I started to doubt my prophetic abilities.

I met my friend in another city, tried talking about goodbyes. I was unable to articulate because the material was unclear. There was something about relating to him in certain ways because he was a man. There was something too that I said was not about him. There was an oblique reference to a feeling borne out of boredom. There was a turning away. There was a sense of being told to turn away. There was a disappointment. There was a different ending.

In New York I was back on edge after months of calm in Austin. It seemed sometimes like nothing had changed, except I was further from old friends. At other times, it seemed that everything had changed, so completely.

Effluent

What if I tell you   no one has ever caught a fish?
What if I tell you   a fish chooses its hook to know what it is
to be acted upon by the gravity?   Writhe as a pendant on the proletariat
necklace of the sea.   What if I tell you there are deplorable ways of killing
a fish than make a medallion out of it? What if I tell you
a fish out of water   dies not because of homesickness
but because there is no home. What if I tell you
the fish searches the nook and corals of the water to find
the hook? What if I tell you fishes complain about the ergonomics
of the hook? What if I tell you   they feel the hook is not personalised
enough for them?   What if I tell you   it means the hook does not fit
in the space provided for?   Fails to dislodge
the occipital lobes. What if I tell you I am committing the same
error I am accusing you of   when I say fishes instead of a fish?
What if I tell you it is ok to lower the mercy of a hook
into the water? What if I tell you the fish prefers the air's cutlass
to the water's vehemence?   What if I tell you this has got nothing
to do with the benthic horror you may have had as a kid? What if I ask you
to drop a bottle of ink into a battle of water but suggest that you
imagine biphenyl poly chloride in the place of ink?
What if I tell you the fish is fluent with your terms.

Shriram Sivaramakrishnan

Reynold

Molly Anders

They say when you're in love, you see your beloved in the faces of strangers. This was not the case with the woman who came down the path. She looked nothing like Reynold, and also I use the word 'woman' with reservations.

'Excuse me, hold on,' I said. 'Did you see a guy in there?' I was at the edge of the park waiting for Reynold, next to the trashcans he'd described in his text message. 'Tall guy, spiky hair? Drunk kind of?'

I have this thing when I'm doing something stupid, I can feel the future two or three seconds in advance, so I winced a split second before her fist sunk into my kidney.

'Do you have any money?'

'The guy does,' I said, hunched over. 'The guy I'm waiting for.'

'Tall spiky drunk guy?'

'Yes,' I said, 'Reynold.'

'We'll wait for him, then.'

She came over and stood next to me. She smelled like a hospital.

'You sure this guy's coming?'

'Nnh.'

'But he's got money?'

'He might.'

'He's big, this guy?'

'He's tall.'

'But big. Is he big?'

I looked at her, or up her, like a tree. 'Not big like you.'

She seemed to like that. She put her hand over her crotch, twisted her hips. Whatever held her up or held her in was giving her trouble.

Something rustled and coughed in the bushes.

'Here he is,' I said. 'Reynold?'

But it wasn't Reynold. It was a skinny man in a tight cap pulled down over his eyebrows. His jaw fluttered.

'Do you have—' he said.

'Here, take that,' the woman held out a cigarette. 'You can have it.'

He took the cigarette. His fingers combed the air for a lighter and I lit him. Then I said it, I don't know why. 'There's a guy coming in a minute, he'll straighten you out.'

The guy's whole body seemed to land softly into this news.

I began to wonder if Reynold could follow through for these people. I wondered what the implications might be for my other kidney if he couldn't.

I thought about the time he left me on the bus on the way out of Shelbyville, asleep across his lap with his balled-up jacket as a pillow. He sacrificed the jacket, just slipped out from under me and got off the bus. It was a nice jacket—three or four dollars in change in the pockets—so he must have really wanted to go.

Or the time he called me Laura by mistake. We were having sex, his eyes were closed. He said 'Laura,' and then opened his eyes—I guess he'd realised what he'd done—but then just went along with it. He turned it into a joke with himself, he said, 'Laura, oh, Laura!' until he came, and then refused to let me come until I called him Laura, too.

Reynold did accounting, and in the evenings he solicited donations for a Jewish NGO. He rang doorbells at dinner time to ask for money. 'Fellowshipping,' he called it. That's how we met. He asked me if I thought the people coming into the country from poor countries were refugees, immigrants or aliens. I said I didn't know. He asked me if I thought foreigners should get health insurance. I said I thought that seemed like a good idea, but could he maybe stop by not at dinner time?

There are some people, like Reynold, that you just can't imagine ever being born, ever having parents. Like they just folded out of themselves one day like a parachute. Reynold claimed he had parents but I never saw them. I did see his cat. He lived with a cat in a small apartment, where he kept a fishtank with the lid off stocked ith tiny blue fish for the cat to claw out and kill on the carpet.

Up ahead, sneakers crunched on the gravel path.

'Reynold?' the tree woman said.

It was another man. He wore a heavy coat and seemed surprised to find us standing there.

'No,' I said. 'That's not Reynold.'

He pulled a gun from an inner pocket. 'I'm going to kill every single one of you motherfuckers,' he said.

'Oh, God, no,' I said. 'No. We're waiting for one more.'

Hearing 'The Boatman's Call' in a Boston Laundromat

When I was 22, my day off was Tuesday,
when I always ding-dinged through
a grimy door on Massachusetts Avenue.

I wore my hair piled high and loose,
jeans frayed, earlobes silver-hooped;
I was always dazed, thirsty, slightly stoned,

hip-hefting the same old basket
filled with the same old clothes.
I never had enough change,

I always had to feed another dollar
to the coin machine, then scoop quarters up from the floor,
and spill-spoon detergent into the drawer.

Through a thin window, I watched it all churn
a frothing muddle, where sometimes, a garment
might become itself, visible only for an instant—

the collar of a work-shirt's fleeting,
blue glance back, or a jeans pocket
kissing its cheek against the glass.

In the dryer, they spiralled damp to dry,
all fly and fall and fall and fly. In the silence
between walkman songs, between spools,

between *(Are You) The One That I've Been Waiting For?*
and *Where Do We Go Now But Nowhere*, all I could see
was washing machines, as though many, many clock-faces

had sprung open to give me a glimpse of inner cogs
and springs, all spinning, all whirring in foamy momentum
every Tuesday afternoon, when I lived in the distance.

Doireann Ní Ghríofa

How Did Books Become Clutter?

Michaële Cutaya

Be careful you're keeping books for the right sentimental reasons
Don't keep books to convey a certain status
If you've got books in your home that you have never read, why are you keeping them?

—Quotes taken from 'How To Get Rid Of Book Clutter,'
on the Home Storage Solutions website.

Some years ago, the house I was living in burnt down with my belongings. Among these, all my books. Like many book owners, I had often cringed at the recommendations of de-cluttering experts and felt they were missing the point of what keeping books was about. Having been through what might be called a radical de-cluttering experience, I thought I could test my assumptions and examine more closely the reasons I keep books.

Let's first say that I felt no sense of liberation—or whatever one is supposed to feel after the de-cluttering process—even though the memory of carrying over one hundred boxes of books was very much alive in my lower back as I had only recently moved into the house-that-burnt. And that I returned to accumulating books quickly afterwards.

Surveying a number of advice columns on the subject I identified what seem to be the three main recurring categories of books we 'should get rid of,' and I tried to unpack how I might relate to them: books we keep for sentimental value, books we keep for status and unread books.

Be careful you're keeping books for the right sentimental reasons

Thinking of keeping books for their sentimental—and possibly monetary—value reminded me of one of my favourite essays: Walter Benjamin's 'Unpacking My Library: A Talk About Book Collecting'. Written in 1931, the essay describes the memories and emotions Benjamin experiences when taking his books out of their crates. He identifies himself as a genuine collector, and in this essay he attempts to convey 'some insight into the relationship of a book collector to his possessions' with a particular focus on the modes of acquisition. He writes that 'every passion borders on the chaotic, but the collector's passion borders on the chaos of memories'; that a collection is 'a disorder to which habit has accommodated itself to such an extent that it can appear as order'. He writes that he made his most memorable purchases on journeys, as a transient, and of the strategies he uses to acquire certain books at auctions to circumvent his limited means. He also writes of the memories of the cities in which he found the books, and suggests that collecting is the most intimate relationship that one can have to objects. He writes of erecting a dwelling with books and disappearing inside.

In his essay 'Unpacking Benjamin and His Library,' Joseph D. Lewandowski compares Benjamin's books to an 'objective constellation of a dynamic past': 'For this library is alive with remembrances, remembrances which are not tucked away, but interrupt, and transmit themselves.'

Whether Benjamin kept his books for the 'right' sentimental reasons is anyone's guess, and reading Benjamin's essay is a whirlwind of insights: one can feel the emotions, and knowing how transient and unstable his life was, one measures all the difficulties he might have encountered to keep a library at all, and how much it might have meant for him. Yes, all this. And yet, this is not it, this is neither the relationship I had with the lost books nor the one I have with those I have gathered since. They were not acquired during exotic travels, and no childhood memories are wrapped up in them.

Don't keep books to convey a certain status

Heavens forbid that I should have books to show off! I could easily dismiss the very thought of it, if only because I have few visitors, and fewer still that enter my workspace where I keep my books. So who would I be showing off to? But past this knee-jerk reaction, it is actually a more interesting question than appears at first. For instance, do we necessarily show off to other people? Can't we ourselves be the audience to whom we are performing? And is aspiring to look better read than we really are or really feel, necessarily a bad thing? Reading Dan Fox's fascinating book *Pretentiousness: Why it Matters* opened up for me new, intriguing ways of thinking about pretention. Fox points to the desire, aspirations and ambitions that are too easily missed when we call someone pretentious, and to the often hidden class prejudice when we mock someone who aspires to be more than they are. Fox reminds us that a pretender's cause is an issue of legitimacy and allegiances and that 'pretending is what kids do to figure out the world.'

With this in mind I rethought my books and my reasons for acquiring some of them. Many years ago, I bought a second hand *Encyclopaedia Universalis*, all twenty volumes of it. Not only was it one of the most expensive objects I had ever owned, it also felt like something to which I had no right, something that could not really belong to me. Aside from libraries, I had only ever encountered these volumes in the homes of friends whose parents were university professors—for a long time the only profession I aspired to—while my parents were school teachers. To own an encyclopaedia was like a game of pretend: those volumes carried a social status that I did not have. It was pretentiousness in all the complexities Fox carefully unpacks, an act of pretend, of mimicry. The encyclopaedia was perhaps the most obvious example, but there are many other such books I bought and read because they represented a certain idea about myself to which I aspired. Eventually I have grown into some of them, enjoying the books for their content and not for the status they conferred. And it is as if I have earned the right to own them—as if I slowly earned the right to my encyclopaedia, the unexplored pages of which still haunt me; it contained such fabulous articles about subjects I did not even know existed. Just browsing through it was like a journey in human knowledge.

There are other books that still loom on the horizon of my ambition, and others that have lost their attraction, because I no longer aspire to the status they confer. So yes I do buy and keep books for status: they are a projection of who I'd like to be, they embody my intellectual ambitions. What's wrong with that?

If you've got books in your home that you have never read, why are you keeping them?

However I may feel about de-cluttering advice generally, suggestions about unread books are those that feel most strange. Unread books are probably at the core of my thoughts about personal libraries. In the de-cluttering genre, they are simply a no-no. You get such advice as: 'Get ruthless with your "yet to read" pile'; 'If it hasn't been read in six months, it probably won't ever be read'; and 'Unread books: "sometime" means "never".' There is even a Japanese word for it, *tsundoku:* '(n.) buying books and not reading them; letting books pile up unread on shelves or floors or nightstands.' The unread books are a species to be eradicated, to be ruthless about, to stop being delusional—pretentious?—about. One always feels somewhat guilty in accumulating unread books.

So coming across Umberto Eco's thoughts in 'How to Justify a Private Library' was a relief for me. Perhaps one important distinction here is between 'people who consider a bookshelf as a mere storage place for already-read books' and those who 'think of the library as a working tool.' Unread books and the private library as a research tool were expanded upon by Nassim Nicholas Taleb—a professor in the Sciences of Uncertainties at the University of Massachusetts—in the opening remarks of his book *The Black Swan: The Impact of the Highly Improbable.* He writes that 'Read books are far less valuable than unread ones' and that a library should contain as much of what we do not know as what we can afford. The more we know, the more the field of what we know we do not know expands, so that as we grow older the number of unread books should grow: 'Indeed, the more you know, the larger the rows of unread books.' He calls this collection of unread books an 'antilibrary,' and describes an 'antischolar' as 'someone who focuses on the unread books, and makes an attempt not to treat his knowledge as a treasure, or even a possession, or even a self-esteem enhancement device—a skeptical empiricist.'

While researching references to Umberto Eco's writings on unread books, I came across an article by Don Trubshaw, 'A Paean to Serendipity,' in which he explores the genealogy of the word serendipity and its importance in research and creativity. He distinguishes serendipity from the accidental and defines it as an aptitude or attitude towards the unexpected within a particular field of human activity. One does not make a discovery in a domain one knows nothing about. Serendipitous discovery takes place in an environment of 'ordered chaos'—such as a library—where unrelated things lie in proximity.

Trubshaw wonders how the use of search engines and digital resources instead of physical libraries and workspaces might impact research, as it might diminish the opportunities for serendipitous encounters:

> Search engines are logical and literal in their search; in order to accommodate new ideas they must be programmed with new search terms. But in this way we are only extending what we already know, or projecting from what we know into the less known. But there is no route into the great realms of ignorance, that which we truly do not know, the ignorance of which we are profoundly ignorant.

This echoes Taleb's notion of the antischolar, focusing on expanding the 'known unknown' rather than the known. As yet, the possibilities for serendipitous discoveries in online research should not be underestimated, but as the pool of data to be mined increases and algorithms become more powerful and more accurate, it is a genuine concern. Trubshaw concludes on the importance of physical working environments:

> Discovery in any enterprise takes place in the messy physicality of the world, whether that is the scientist's lab, the artist's studio or the writer's desk, through immersion in the discourse of the discipline and problematic issues to which one is dedicated to finding a solution.

This physical environment that maps out what I know I do not know, that visual reminder of all these fields of knowledge to which I aspire, these get to the heart of why I acquire and keep books and why I will always find more walls to shelve.

The personal library is like a mind map, one organised by ever shifting constellations: the books are arranged by author, by subject, by collection, by their size or by the colour of the cover; they are re-arranged by being drawn together towards a particular research topic—this very essay has triggered the formation of new constellations, bringing new books onto the shelves and re-arranging existing ones.

So losing my books, journals, photocopies and all the written traces I keep around me at all time, triggered a form of amnesia: I lost the books that remained as traces of past inquiries, and the books that marked future domains of exploration; the past and the future of my thoughts. I am only slowly recovering from this amnesia, as I cross over some of these paths—those taken and those I aspired to—and remember the books that marked them.

The day after the fire, a book I had ordered arrived in the post. I had ordered it as part of a particular arrangement of books and ideas, a particular area of research. It was now the only book I owned. I held in my hands, looking at it and it made no sense, there was no shelves for it to go, no companions to join. To this day, I am not sure what to do with that book: it belongs to an assemblage that no longer exists and does not quite fit any of the new ones.

It took me some weeks before I was able to buy books again—probably one of the longest lapses in my book acquisition history. And the first books I bought were a dictionary and a thesaurus. I felt I could not really go wrong there.

I sometimes wonder what this current concern with organising, tidying, de-cluttering is a symptom of. It is supposed to make us more efficient and productive—but then what if messy environments make us more creative, as some research seems to suggest?

According to the de-cluttering guru Marie Kondo, the work of tidying is to identify the things that make you happy. In her bestselling book *The Life-Changing Magic of Tidying Up: The Japanese Art of Decluttering and Organising*, she enjoins us to keep only those things that 'spark joy' —from the Japanese 'tokimeku,' which translates as flutter, palpitate or throb. And here I can only agree with her, at least as far as my books are concerned. Each and every one of them—the read, the partly read and the unread alike—'spark joy,' not only in the Japanese sense but also in the Spinozian sense of joy. According to Spinoza, joy is the feeling or affect that characterises the passage to a greater perfection, the increase of the power of acting: we feel joy when our power to act and our capacity to be affected increase. The books in my library increase my power to act, as a researcher, and my capacity to be affected in their constant reminder of what I know I don't know—which I only wish to expand. Few other things give me such joy, least of all a shelf-less wall.

Parrot
Nicole Flattery

When she thought about the second woman—and she had distantly when she'd been younger; how her life could potentially be upended by someone she didn't know—it was always with a sort of black amusement. And when she said things that were improper—lines about her current situation that were just slightly off, the dry delivery of which was the reason why her friends were her friends—she had to admit, if only to herself, that she never imagined she would be the second woman.

That afternoon, still within their first six months in Paris, she went to an art exhibition. Exhibitions were something she was trying, attempting to adjust to: their sophistication, their unique shush. She moved up and down the staircase, cheapening the place with the cut of her clothes, searching for her soul at a frantic pace that suggested she was rummaging through a demolition site for the remains of her belongings rather than spending a pleasant few hours in a museum. She was not alone. The boy was with her, suspended from school for the day, a fact to which he was largely indifferent. At only nine years old he had learned to handle disappointment and failure with the sort of grace that, in her early thirties, still escaped her. He set the tone for the afternoon, ignoring her under the pretence of looking at paintings of nondescript benches. In a corner of the exhibition, there was a cage with two stuffed parrots. The woman spent an unnatural amount of time staring at them. They seemed as if they had been there forever, loving and admiring each other. How could they leave? They were behind bars. Nobody knew what happened in the tiny parameters of their cage.

Recently, at a dinner party, with her husband's new colleagues she had—seized by the closeness of the couple, the sudden tininess of their Parisian apartment—explained that at home, in the Irish countryside, all of the houses were built far apart, with long driveways, so you could easily get away from your family. She did the smooth, fluid motion of a driveway with her hands.

'They are legally obliged to be that way,' she said.

Afterwards, she felt stupid, like she had revealed more than she intended. The woman half of the couple, wearing heavy, intimidating jewellery that implied intellectual heft, suggested that perhaps that was only in her family. Perhaps, she agreed. Therapy, she considered, as she flipped through the art books in the gift shop—their pages full of unnerving, confusing beauty—was also something new she could try.

As they walked back through the city streets, the October cold not wholly unpleasant, the boy sloped two steps behind her, but in her eyeline, always in her eyeline. As they strolled, history announcing itself at every corner, she answered a call from her mother. Since they had moved, her mother rang a lot and spoke at her usual steady stream, like she was being held hostage and needed to get all the information out before her throat was slit. The woman understood this way of speaking only after she became a mother herself. She would barely be recovered from one of these conversations when another would happen. Her mother was retired and bored. What was she supposed to do now? What was she supposed to do in that house? Just thinking about it made her want to get another job.

'Don't do that,' the woman said, 'start going to exhibitions. I've just been to one.'

'I thought you didn't like art.'

'I don't like artists. There's a difference.'

When she let herself and the boy into the apartment they were renting, all the apartments built discreetly into the architecture of the city as if to obscure the fact that families lived in them at all, there was a notice on the front door. It was a picture, not unlike those in the exhibition, but less celebrated, of two cockroaches, one on the left, one on the right, with X's running vertically through their bodies. There were some words promising there had been cockroaches and now they were gone, or there was an ongoing effort to get rid of the cockroaches. She wasn't sure. She didn't read or speak French. Later, in bed, with her husband, under crisp, ironed sheets, she tried to sleep off the possibility of cockroaches.

'I love you,' he whispered.

She blinked anxiously in the dark, as if trying to identify something. 'Go easy on that stuff,' she advised him.

*

Maybe the problem was that she was tired. She had been a bit tired when she entered art college, but dropping out had exhausted her. She remembered the final meeting, her prepared speech about why she was leaving, the made-up family reasons; then interrupting herself; then, finally, silence.

'You should leave if you're unhappy,' they said.

'I'm unhappy because I don't think I belong here.'

Nobody begged her. It was cute that she had tried in the first place. She put the sculptures she had made in her first year in her parents' garage and her mother used them to hang up wet clothes.

This was a serious decision but she didn't know it until a few years later. She stayed in Dublin to work, sharing shabby rooms with a series of men. Through these relationships she wanted to prove something, prove that she was still complicated and interesting without a degree, but there was no time. She was too busy picking up after her boyfriends, making disappointed faces, listening to them complain about the inconsequences of their actions. She felt like a mother forcefully pushed on stage in a farce, with only an apron and a spatula. Why wouldn't they let her commit the delinquency she knew she was capable of?

Why was she always standing next to the delinquents, apologetically shaking her head? All these relationships ended the exact same way, with circuitous conversations and dully rational arguments, as if both participants were politicians lobbying for their own happiness. Denied even heartbreak and animosity, the modern emphasis was on the demonstration of respect, however insincere. In her last relationship, before she met her husband, he respected her so much he let her pay for everything. 'This is respectful,' she thought as she paid their rent, as her credit card hit the illuminated screen again and again. When he ended it, she felt like she had been mugged—mugged of money, but also of time.

'I still respect you,' he said.

'I don't care if you do or you don't.'

'But I do,' he said earnestly, 'I really do.'

She was so tired.

He moved his stuff out and she continued doing the scrambling necessary to staying alive; working two jobs in the city, her personality dissolving into small talk. The cost of travel, the cost of lunch, the cost of being young.

She met her husband in an office where she was a temp, the irony not lost on her, irony never lost on her. She treated these temp jobs like cocktail parties, draping her sparkling self across surfaces, trying to dazzle in a limited amount of time. He devastated her with the ease that he saw through her. He filed away her exaggerations, her evasions, the playfulness that was beginning to curdle into meanness so he could eventually embarrass her—a child in an adult place. When, one lunchtime, through a mouthful of sandwich, she laughed at a man in the office, because every office must have someone sad to laugh at, he frowned at her.

'That man is depressed.'

'How do you know that?" she asked.

'How do you not?'

She drafted an email where she declared it was up to her what she decided was funny. Instead, she offered to buy him a drink. She hadn't meant what she said. She explained, in careful email language, that she was beginning to suspect she might be a bad person. She had dropped out of college and there had been a number of other severe and deranged fuck-ups. Several weeks later, nudging, overly-friendly correspondence passing between them daily, he kissed her for the first time, his hands touching the back of her neck. They always went to the same B&B, the same room, fringed lamps and light curtains. It was like an affair made on an assembly line, everyone playing their part, following a strict pattern. No poetry, no sunlight on the bedsheets. The only surprise was when she found, unbelievably, like discovering a hidden room in a house, that she was in love with him. They only had one discussion about his wife, and it barely qualified as a discussion. She was ill and had been for a long time. Her illness would never be over. He had done everything he could. She believed him, not because he was a man who could ever be accused of heartlessness, but because he looked like someone who had begged and cried and tried to reassemble and done everything he could.

*

The winter in Paris, two days before Halloween, grew harsh and the woman's lips cracked what felt like audibly. She was concerned strangers on the metro could hear, as if her mouth was a strip of velcro to be peeled open and closed. She knew she should be worried about presentation, in a city that demanded presentation, but she sloughed the dead skin off, forced her teeth into the supple, comforting grooves. Smiling was the only communication available to her and, overnight, it had turned ugly. Still, she continued smiling, amiably, like a tourist, like a secretary, like a combination of both—a tourist's secretary.

She was called to the boy's school, English-speaking, private, already more than they could afford, at least once a week. She went because she wasn't working and for other, more defiant reasons. The school was a monstrous structure on a street of other dutiful buildings, including a police station, their insides deep and hidden. The boy had behavioural problems, concentration issues, the whole catalogue. She had humorous lines prepared about how they were more alike than they knew, how she might be his mother after all, but the teacher never gave her a single opportunity. Every Monday or Friday, the woman sat in a child's chair and struggled for a position that lent her some dignity. She could offer nothing concrete—that his behaviour would improve or that she would insist it improve. Her presence there only promised she would be at the next meeting and the meeting after that, all the way to graduation and beyond. And although it made both her and the teacher uneasy in a way they couldn't articulate, she had to come in to prove her worth, her plans to stay.

He had been caught stealing from another boy's pockets.

'Maybe he was just curious about what was in the pockets. Curious,' she repeated, hopefully.

The teacher gave her a stern look, violently shrinking, and the woman wondered who educated these people, schooled them in disapproval. 'That wasn't it,' the teacher said. She was from London and had a soundless way of communicating disappointment. Their relationship never moved beyond professional; they never hinted at their personal lives, as if any friendliness might cause embarrassment the next time they saw each other, and there would be a next time.

The woman pulled a face that was also learned, perfected from years of bad relationships—let down but doubtful of change.

'I will speak to him,' she said, finally.

On the metro, hurtling home through black tunnels, he sat beside her, always content in her company. He kept up a steady chatter about school as if constant talk could distract from his misdemeanour. She was familiar with this trick. If she ever tried to grab his hand, he shook her off. He never allowed her to touch him. When she watched the other mothers exit through the school gates—in their discreet, mother uniforms; this city believed in uniforms—pushing their sons' hair back from their eyes, casually shepherding them, her mind raced with thoughts of self-improvement. She should try to be gentler, less agitated, learn to make small talk in another language, or even her own language. Become someone a boy might want to touch. It seemed as if her whole life, from the age of thirteen onwards, had been geared towards that rotten desire and now the world had come up with a genius way of punishing her.

She tried to tempt him into a pastry shop, bribe him into confessing with sugar. It was gloomy. It was also possibly criminal.

'No, thanks,' he said, massaging his abdomen, his body so tiny that it was hard to believe that it contained the correct amount of organs. 'Sports.'

'Sports.'

'Sports,' he repeated and raced ahead of her.

She considered, not for the first time, becoming one of those mothers who carries fruit with them everywhere, pulling it out of the insides of their handbags like a magic trick, eternally resourceful. On the front door, beside the cockroaches, although she tried not to look, tried not to be confronted with her own ignorance of the French language too often, was a notice with a photo of a rat, no X running through it, free to do what he pleased. It was a vicious rat, his tiny teeth bared. He looked motivated.

When the boy went to the bathroom, she flicked through his phone, the one concession they allowed him. There was never anything of concern, just a sadness attached to it, a lonely phone gasping for contact. She watched the clips he had recorded from the police station across the road from the school, his newest fascination. Blue-uniformed boys wandered blurrily back and forth, groups of two or three, trying to look busy or brave, or both. They were armed in a traumatised city, their hands resting on their guns as if the gesture alone could reassure what happened before would never happen again. There were only five clips, shaky and accompanied by the raucous playground laughter of boys, but she watched them to the end.

*

The first time his wife called the police the woman went to the station with her own mother. They drove in silence. In the reception, they sat side-by-side and her mother advised her to just be herself, as if that—the whole process of being herself—wasn't exactly why she was here in the first place. They waited in the exact same way, patiently, showing no hint of irritation, both betraying their own telltale signs of anxiety—her mother rummaged constantly in her handbag, the woman ran her fingers over greasy patches of her skin. A policewoman smiled gently at them, before beckoning the woman into a room. The woman remembered how she and her mother used to go to the bogs, weekend rebellions, the two of them running wild, comfortable in the dirt. Once, she slipped into a trench and had only managed to wade through the deep muck with her mother's careful encouragement. The walk from one side of the station to the other was like that.

In the small, airless room she was told they had received a phone call from his wife. Her car had allegedly been stolen and the woman was the prime suspect, the only suspect. The doubt was in the allegedly. She knew that a policewoman was being used for her sensitivity, and she wondered how many sensitive cases she had to handle a week, and how much sensitivity she had left. The policewoman's shirt was untucked, her eyes heavily ringed, her shoulders drooped; all those crime-free hours spent at pedestrian crossings, waiting in cars, weighing on her, transforming her waistline. The woman thought she looked ridiculous. When the policewoman placed a hand over hers and declared it a domestic situation, her dislike didn't alleviate. There was no decency in the movement, only the desire to dominate.

'We can't throw you in jail,' she said, with a tight, mean smile, just for being a silly girl.'

'Why?' she asked, 'Not enough room?'

The policewoman scowled at her.

'I'm sorry,' she said, 'I'm so tired.'

On the way back, her mother pulled the car into a quiet stretch of motorway so she could cry freely, tears vandalising her face, emotion she didn't know she had left in her. Her mother let her cry, even allowed her to veer into self-pity, before she asked was she upset because the police didn't think she could rob a car. They laughed despite themselves, a dark hollow-sized trench hiding inside it, surprised they were still capable of making the sound.

The second time his wife reported a made-up crime, he went alone. He explained that after the birth of their son, his wife had developed postnatal depression, then just depression, the regular kind. So she can be difficult sometimes, the police said. When he came home to the house they were now renting together outside Dublin—in an estate of identical houses so alike that she often arrived at the wrong door—the back of his work shirt was soaked, and he was shaken in his own unshakeable way. In the middle of the night, he woke up, his breath sour, and told her he didn't like the word difficult, had never liked it. They didn't smile then, they wouldn't dare, but there were still whispered jokes between them, in trouble with the law, like two teenagers on the lam.

The third time the police got involved in their lives, they went together. A teacher had discovered bruising on the boy's body, still and silent purple lakes, signs of abuse. After an investigation that moved slow, then fast, everything being worked out in rooms that didn't include them, the boy's mother was declared unfit and he was sent to live with them permanently. 'By who?' the woman wanted to ask, 'declared an unfit mother by who?' They had a few interactions with the same policewoman from her first encounter, the police seemingly attached to them now. She sometimes looked at the woman like she forgave her. This makes it easier for you. You must be happy now.

They married in an embarrassed ceremony shortly before they went to Paris. It was a year after the funeral; he changed suits. Her friends donned confused formalwear. She was having them on, right? No one could be this in love, no one could make this sacrifice. Certainly not her. They thought the production of her life, always entertaining, was never going to end. She spent a lot of time in the bathroom, avoided the food, searched for her mother's features in her own when they stood side-by-side in the mirror. Throughout all of this, the boy said almost nothing and she watched him like he was a crucial witness. Everything she knew about him was mediated through others, his teacher, his father, guards.

He had to speak sometime though. That was the deal in this life—no matter how much you tried to avoid it, you had to speak sometime.

In the weeks before the ceremony, in bed, still her boyfriend then, fiancée if she felt like being technical, both terms startlingly trite for what they were trying, he held her tightly in his sleep as if she was going to sneak out. A restless one-night stand. His grief had been huge, paralysing, and the guilt was worse; finding lists, in his handwriting, of what he could have done. So they put a ban on sadness, binned newspapers, left the television on cartoons of pink hyperactivity. Grief had a time frame and when they reached that time frame, and he wasn't recovered and neither was his son, money was the problem. If they had money, they could somehow circumnavigate the time frame. He was in numbers and was constantly trying to beat the morose odds, trying to outrun a train. He wanted to make her happy. It was her turn to be happy. People were the problem for a while, general people and then, more specifically, this country. This country was going to make him exercise, this country was going to make him get up early, this country was going to make him put a brave face on it. Let's go somewhere, he said, that makes miserable a look, that smiles only when it absolutely has to.

'Paris,' she said.

She bought a guidebook and flipped through it before bed. It was just pictures of macarons and rich, oppressive buildings. There was no guidance in it. At night, she curled her body into a promise, in answer to his clawing question, that she wouldn't leave them.

*

There was occasionally something so cheerfully immoral about the city it caught her off-guard, made her feel like her former self. Go and have an absurd love affair, it told her. Go on. You've done it before. Do it again. Walk around naked underneath your coat. She considered the possibility that everyone was naked underneath their coats. It wouldn't surprise her. The city was silent during the day and loud in the evenings, and the sudden transition alarmed her. It could be bossy in that way—be scared, don't be scared, now be terrified. Once the metro came to a stop, the lights died, total silence, not even a cough. Then it moved as normal. There was the sense of an unspoken resilience. Every Monday or Friday, regardless of where she was, how unpredictable she was feeling, she received a phone call from the school. This was what she talked about when she rang home. In a city of novelties, responsibility was the only real novelty.

It was Halloween when she next stepped into the boy's school, passing by unremarked except for a few fake skeletons dangling from the ceiling, an unsophisticated holiday. When she stood in the hallway, feeling like a student herself, the place spoke to her of sweat and failure. Already, at under twelve, there were violin, piano, language lessons abandoned, a sluggishness set in. A sea of uniforms swept over her; a tide of blue. The boys all had bad posture and awkward gaits as if ashamed of their childhoods. Why are you so sluggish, she wanted to ask. Perk up. Many of you are going to be rich.

'What's the collective name for a group of boys?' she asked the teacher.

'In French or in English?'

'English.'

'I don't know in either language.'

'A school of boys, maybe,' the woman said, 'a drooping of boys.'

The teacher always so elegant, yet merciless, in her admissions, told her that morning the boy had hit a classmate—slapped him hard across the face for beating him at a race.

The woman was quiet for a moment. 'He doesn't get this from me.'

'No,' she said, delicately.

'I'm the stand-in.'

The teacher gave a curt nod in response.

She leaned forward awkwardly in her chair. 'You think I'm not trying.'

'I don't think that.'

'I love that boy.'

'I know you do.'

A silence passed.

'We don't want to have to expel him.'

'I will speak to him,' she said, 'I will speak to him.'

'He's very good at running,' the teacher said, a genuine smile on her face. 'Fast.'

'He does get that from me,' she said and closed the door.

In the hallway she waited for him, watched the overhead skeletons, seemingly relaxed without a skin. She spun one in her hand, made it dance. It seemed to resent the movement. A private school, she thought, its skeleton private.

On the way home they stopped at the playground beside an imposing church. The city constantly humbled her, reminding her at every opportunity that people had been there before, waving its hands around in excitement about its incredible history. It was irritating. Out of his schoolbag the boy took out a drawing of a ghost, the eyes far apart, in opposite hemispheres. Squiggles representing horror. She wasn't sure if he was proud of it.

'That's a beautiful picture,' she said, cautiously.

'No, it's not.'

'No,' she agreed, laughing, 'it's not.'

She sat on the wooden bench, her breath rippling out in stubborn, icy waves in front of her. She watched him climbing, tried to spot any trace of athletic talent. Then she watched for what she was told to watch for—any signs of trauma, impulse toward sadness. How could you know now? She never socialised with the other mothers. It was ridiculous, her attitude problem resurfacing. She felt they knew she had been coerced at the last minute, didn't have the correct paperwork. She had never held him as a baby, never heard him cry, a cooing from another world. She once listened to sounds of babies crying and decided which one he would have sounded most like. It was a high-pitched, argumentative wailing. She went on the websites with the mothers of newborns, introduced herself. There were some genuine points of interest but nothing to help with a nine-year old.

'Are you a troublemaker?' she asked when he, out-of-breath, sat down.

'No.'

'That's what troublemakers say.' She rested her arm behind him. 'Tell me about running.'

'It's stupid.'

'I like stupid things.'

'You like stupid things?'

'Yeah, I like stupid things,' she said loudly, finding freedom in it, 'That's why they kicked me out of college.'

'You got *kicked out*?'

'I kicked myself out. But it was the same thing. Tell me.'

It was fun, he explained, it was good, but to be the best you had to keep practicing and what was the point? It was a version of the argument she had with herself daily. She wanted to encourage him but what was she supposed to do? Tell him, like a dog, to sit down, stand up, kneel? She had no authority. Why was she even here? What did she want from it all—a medal?

On the metro, at the last stop, she asked him outright. 'Why did you hit that boy?'

'The medal,' he said simply.

On the front door she stuck the picture of the ghost and drew a large, deliberate X.

That night, in bed, her husband described his day and she listened. He was in love with the city, wandered around in a loving daze. The distance was good for him and, although his work was difficult, obscure, he was now a medium shade of grey, instead of a deep shade.

'How did you know it would be right?' he asked.

'I know everything,'

She had been to Paris once before with her mother when she was twenty, a few months after she dropped out and it didn't look like she was going back. She had settled into the rhythms of the joke but her mother knew, instinctively, without having to be told, how disappointed she was. It was a cheap trip; they shared a hotel room. Their room contained a tiny, electric Eiffel Tower. They were women who knew dirt, country roads, had learned to make conversation in corner shops, confronted, finally, by glamour, by seriousness. They did everything wrong. They went to the wrong bars, the wrong restaurants, the wrong streets. She wasn't sure they saw Paris at all, neither of them exactly clear on what a holiday was. They fought on several street corners, made up, and hid their giddy laughter behind their hands. The city was impatient with them. What is so funny, it asked. What could possibly be so funny? Her mother made her go to every museum and when her feet were sore she waited in the cafes. She remembered seeing her across the crowded room, her soles exposed, sitting patiently, waiting for her daughter, looking like an old woman.

'You will make a great old woman,' she told her mother that night.

'I am an old woman,' her mother said.

Later, in their twin beds, she asked her mother was she hard to raise.

'You had an answer for everything. Everything.'

'I don't anymore. Not at all.'

Then her mother, a shadow on the wall of the hotel room, told her that she regretted some of her life. The usual. She would have liked to do more, although she didn't really know what: live in European countries, make mistakes. She never had the time to figure out what it was. She felt her life was small, mechanical. She spoke for a while.

'I shouldn't have said all that,' she decided, after a thoughtful pause.

'It's okay,' the woman said, 'it's fine.'

'I had a nice time.'

'I had a nice time too.'

They fell asleep, after a while, Paris coming through the slats of the hotel blinds.

*

She only saw the boy's mother once. It was the woman's fault for recognising her, for being too thorough in her investigations, combing through photographs—looking for what exactly? Evidence that he had adored her, evidence that she had once been someone you could adore. It was in a hardware shop, the woman had gone to buy some paint. She wandered through the shop, marvelling at the anarchic presentation, broken pieces of domesticity everywhere, a sink just sitting in the middle of the floor. It was a joke shop, everything too large or ominous or numerous, hundreds of versions of the same thing, everything gesturing towards a great future. In the lighting section she turned a lamp on and off, imagined it on her bedside table, a matching one opposite, lamps came in pairs. She was decorating the house, no longer able to look at the white walls. It was in the paint aisle, staring businesslike at the selection, that she felt the boy's mother. It occurred to her that they were both standing in front of a wall of paint and that if they had been two different women, they could have been standing in the glow of a painting, a scene that would at least lend some ceremony. But they weren't, and they weren't. The tins of paint stretched far back into the wall. She glanced at the boy's mother sideways, but didn't fully look at her, because she knew then she would have to look at her twice, to see if she could tell from her face, from the planes of it, the missed medication and the locked cabinets and the attempts with the kitchen bleach. In exactly a week the boy's mother would be dead, succeeding at what she had been trying for a lot of her life. The woman didn't turn her head. She looked fixedly ahead and felt the boy's mother only as a presence. She wanted to apologise, explain that she hated it all too, fake pleasantness and being alive and fucking paint, that nobody blamed her, but when she looked around, she was gone. It was like a dream and, afterwards, in the car, the paint on her lap, the light came through the windshield blindingly strong, like in a dream.

*

When she got a chance she went to cafes and pretended to be a tourist, a woman with a book and a coffee. That afternoon, underneath the coffee, she could smell the boy's laundry on her—the clothes she had washed and dried earlier. In the long mirror that wrapped around the cafe, she watched herself, not like her idea of a mother, but when she smiled, resolved to smile, the face that looked back was her own mother's. In the cafe, a parade of faces worked at their food and drink. A man walked around with a baby, clutching him to his chest. Her husband's colleagues told her after it first happened, you could see people quietly scanning the exits in bars and restaurants. How long would it take to escape? One minute? Two minutes? She waited for the call and, when it came, she went to the school. On the metro she thought about how easy it would be to step off somewhere else, disappear. It occurred to her that, for the whole of her life, she might never stop having that thought.

'I haven't seen you in ages,' she said to the teacher.

'It was three days ago.'

'I know.'

'It was three days ago. I remember, believe me.' There was the flicker of a bold smile.

'I admire your relentless professionalism.'

'Thank you.'

She walked behind the teacher, following the clip-clop of her work heels through the long corridor of identical lockers. They walked up several flights of stairs, until they came to a door marked 'No Entry.' They entered. Inside there was nothing, a couple of disused ping-pong tables, some broken furniture. At the front there was a curtain.

'I thought you might like to watch,' the teacher said and pushed back the curtain, revealing a pane of glass, opening, miraculously, into light.

The woman came closer to the glass and leaned against it. Below, in the gym, a class was happening. She saw the fierce shape of a coach in the centre. On scattered blue mats rested the bodies of twenty boys, small heads, small bodies, in various states of stretching. She searched for the boy and found him, his body taut, ready to launch, and she held her breath.

The Pin Tin

In the wicker basket she had lifted down
were trim cotton reels, a black needle cloth,
and an orange disc tin with planets, stars,
and the whoosh of a rocket on the lid.

I was let play with it—carefully though—
while she got ready to mend a thorn-rip,
a gravel-ragged knee, or a mend itself,
a jumper-cuff I'd encouraged to fray.

There was always a slight prick, when the lid came off,
that it wasn't filled with sweets or money.
But as she sat under the brighter side-light,
the damage in her lap, and me at her feet

picking over the pin tin—the thin ones
and red bobble-tops, smooth as Jupiter
when I plumped them between finger and thumb—
I would look up from the glints and silvers

for the wetted end lining up to the eye;
that still, before she was in to her work,
that still I wouldn't give, when the memory
threads me, for all the riches of heaven.

Iain Twiddy

Crescent

Susanne Stich

I. It'll be a shower scene. No Hitchcock, though. Just you, standing there, under the trickle of soothing hot water. Thin, but not too thin, shampoo in your hair, yesterday's underwear on the green rug outside the steamed-up cabin. A mini break by the sea, three years into your marriage. A spring morning, one of the sunniest days yet, a full moon still visible in the sky. You're humming to yourself, but the fan is on, so nobody can hear you, the landlady downstairs, your husband next door.

'Take your time,' he said before you disappeared into the bathroom.

Among a handful of other reasons, you married him because he reassures you like this. And this morning, it's precisely what you do: you take your time moving around the cracks of your life. The previous night, in a cosy bar in the harbour, you danced. Nothing spectacular, a few groovy moves to some nice R&B music. You're right, you won't be a ballerina, but your husband enjoys watching you. What's more, he knows when you're happy, and, on the whole, at that particular time of your life, you are. After the humming, however, you slip. The shower cabin is small, so you don't fall very far. Remembering the past in a confined space, it's what adults do, and you are no exception. Your arm hurts, you expect a bruise, assume its disappearance down the line, a week later, maybe two, nothing drastic. Disoriented, your arm throbbing, you press both palms against the shower wall to steady yourself. You start spotting pink patches of mould between the tiles, first one, then two, then many more, streaking the cabin walls like weak blood.

Before you know it, water cascades into memory, days spent silent as a child, your pale father next door, smoking and watching TV, waiting for nothing, changing in the wrong direction, almost taking you with him. Afterwards, in the hospital, during your worst spell, aged fourteen, with staff keeping the place spotless, there wasn't any mould. They even tried to make you spotless, and still, while nobody dared to believe it for months, especially you, one day they sent you home alive, ready to become someone who, years later, would work, travel, marry. If you remember one thing in that shower, make it this. In the meantime, you look up into the showerhead's tiny holes. They remind you of a microscope through which you looked at dead flies as a child. Under the lens, the insects took on the texture of a Dürer drawing, clear lines, grey and black, a scaffolding of existence.

All in all your shower scene only lasts minutes, and minutes go fast in your thirties. Afterwards, you massage the bruised spot with a towel. Your husband sits on his side of the bed, looking through emails, deleting most of them. You don't tell him a thing, you manage just perfectly, and the thought makes you proud, stand tall. You get dressed, dry your hair, put on mascara. You go downstairs with him, have breakfast, then head to the beach, all set to watch people fly kites.

II. Right now, all this is far away. You're a child, eleven years old. It's night-time, the end of December. In a different country, the one you were born in, in a city flat on the fifth floor, you and your father have just finished watching TV. A new series, made for the Christmas season. There are six episodes altogether, one per night, leading up to New Year's Eve. So far you've seen three, and during each of them, at some point, your father cried. He stubbed out his cigarette, sobbed a little, and finally wiped his eyes with his sleeve. The series tells of a young ballet dancer's recovery from a traumatic accident. By now the girl has recuperated enough that she is slowly starting to dance again. She has a barre in her bedroom and goes to class every day. What's more, you know that before the end of the final episode, just before the start of another year, the same girl will be given the lead in an important production, go abroad, and fall in love. You've read about it in the TV magazine.

After tonight's episode you ask your father to follow you into your room. You want to show him a picture of the girl you cut out of the magazine. When he finally manages to shuffle into your room and lowers himself onto the chair by the desk, you aren't sure anymore it is such a good idea. Besides, he doesn't ask what you were going to show him. He simply looks relieved to be seated. Hard chairs are easier for him than soft seats. You sit on the bed across from him, cross-legged, fakir-like, atop your favourite duvet covers, a sea of horses, brown and yellow, with soulful eyes. In your room your father isn't allowed to smoke. It's not your rule, it's your mother's, and he abides by it. When he doesn't say anything, you start counting the horses, but there's always a point when you get mixed up. There are so many of them, their pattern random. After a while you don't remember the ones you have already counted.

Just before the episode started he sent you for a packet of Camels from the cigarette machine around the corner.

'Quick, honey… quick,' he said, his shaky left hand counting the coins into your palm. You put on your winter coat, zipped it up and ran out of the flat.

'And don't you smoke when you grow up,' you heard him call after you, and you shook your head skipping down five flights of stairs. You shook your head because he generally likes it when you acknowledge that he's spoken, even if he couldn't see you right then. You ran through the darkness like someone with a kite, inexplicably connected to the thing that animates all, the thing that was nearly knocked out of him, and has never quite come back, leaving him like a halfway house. A minute or two later, when you stopped to throw the coins into the machine, the Camels came out with a thud. You picked them up, a girl with no gloves on, who routinely shakes her head for her father as if to prove to him that her life will be better than his. You ran back home through the freezing cold, the stars above you like moments to come, the third episode about to start.

Your father is a small man, and his story entirely different from the girl's in the series. He could have been a jockey, though. A stranger told him this when he was a boy, on a Saturday afternoon, somewhere in the city, when all was in ruin after the war. The sun was high in the sky when the stranger said this, and afterwards your father spent some weeks trying to find out about jockeys, but nobody knew much about them, other than that they had to be thin. The stranger never returned, and it turned out that instead of becoming a jockey, your father had to learn to write again in his forties.

These days, when he needs to sign a form or one of your school reports, he insists on using a poorly flowing biro from his office days. When you offer him your fountain pen, he hisses, like an iron putting out steam. Slowly, the words emerge on paper, small, restricted outlines, like housing for the poor. When he was first sent to rehab, two and a half years ago, in a small town in the foothills of the Alps, he sent you a postcard with the picture of a cheerful Alsatian. His letters were much more neatly printed back then, like arrows into the future.

Liebe Marie, ...

You've hated Alsatians since you were three and nearly attacked by one. It ran toward you one rainy morning and bared its teeth. It didn't bark or howl, it just ran, as if you were the only thing worth running toward in the whole wide world. Your father managed to pick you up at the last moment, but he must have forgotten this when he sent the card five years later. He has forgotten many things.

'You can't blame him for that, sweetie,' your mother says.

A stroke peels layers off a person, makes them smaller, absent-minded at times. They look at you more, spend more time trying to say things than managing to say them. Your father is just one of many.

You've seen them, small crowds in the hospital, the rehabilitation centres, the support groups.

None of your friends have ever mentioned that their fathers cry. In the books you read there's no mentioning of crying fathers either. And even in the new TV series, when the girl had the accident, her father didn't shed any tears. The doctor says that your father cries because of the medication. It's a side effect. What's more, regardless of whether he cries or not, your father doesn't like being watched. That's why you've developed ways of not looking without missing a thing. Right now, as he sits in your room, you scan his frail body with the paunch at the front, his sad, faintly red face, wondering if you'll become like him some day rather than the dancer you wanted to show him a picture of. In the end, lost for something better to do, you press down the play button on your cassette player. You don't know which song is up next, and then, after a brief spell of static noise, The Beatles' 'I'll Follow the Sun' begins. With the winter darkness outside, the refrain makes you giggle. Your father listens, then looks at you and giggles, too. After that he cries a little, no big deal. There are voices and laughter next door in the kitchen. Your mother, your uncle, aunt and three cousins are playing cards, trusting that you and your father will return to them soon. After all it is Christmas, and the family at Christmas is all about love. Like a slice of cake that doesn't get smaller, a cake you and your father had a little too much of.

Later, when the guests are gone, with your mother asleep, and your father back in the living room, watching more TV on his own, some of which will make him cry all over again, you'll look at the picture of the girl on your own. You'll take in her long neck, the burgundy leotard, the carefully braided hair, piled up in an impressive do, and know in your bones that you will never be like her. What's more, chances are your father will never go back to work, never walk like he used to. Your family have lived like this for nearly three years now, three springs into summers, autumns, winters, too long to pretend.

'He's never sailed smoothly through life,' your aunt said about him once, not long before he got ill. Her words made you picture him in a little red boat on the open sea, a film that doesn't end well. A storm flares up, the boat keels over, your father disappears amongst crashing waves. The sun is about to set, no one hears his screams but the gulls above. You prefer it when you manage to reduce the film to a still, a boat surrounded by tiny waves, far enough away for you not to see the exact look on your father's face. You walk in and out of the image, looking on from the beach, mostly to check he is still in the boat.

In the mornings it is your mother who empties the ashtrays. She doesn't like it when you do it.

'You're a child, remember? This is what adults do. Adults only, Marie.'

If you had a choice to be somebody else, it would have to be the girl in the series, but you will never be like her of course. You keep forgetting, even if now, at eleven years of age, it's obvious. You still love contorting your body on the living room carpet. It makes your mother and father go 'Ooh' and 'Aah', and 'Our daughter, the acrobat.' You don't want them to stop, and you bend your body some more. You twist it until it hurts and you finally remember that you're wasting your time.

'I'm fat,' you told your parents last week.

'You must be joking, you're a rake,' your mother replied.

'What's a rake?'

'It's a saying.'

'It's awful!'

'How about a toothpick instead?' she teased.

You pulled a disgusted face. Your father was watching.

'Well, something different then. Let me think,' your mother said.

She looked at you long and hard, but you still felt fat, even if you weigh less than you should. You've been told. People have taken you aside. 'Eat more, you must eat more, don't worry about your Papa,' they plead.

'You're like a crescent moon,' your father suddenly filled the silence, 'how about that?'

It stopped you in your tracks. You didn't know what he meant, but he'd said it beautifully, without hesitation, and you didn't want to ask any questions. Even your mother looked a little confused, but eventually she smiled, and your father's sentence hovered in the room for the rest of the afternoon.

You'll remember it again in bed tonight, just before switching off the light. It will make you climb back out of bed, open the French doors and step out on the balcony. Slippers on your feet, a small, luminous thing, your winter coat over your pyjamas fluorescent against the sky, you'll look at the lit up medieval castle on the hill in the distance. In three days' time, on New Year's Eve, fireworks will go off at midnight. They'll look spectacular, the castle far enough away to seem just the right size for you to pick it up and hold it in your hands, like a snow globe or a shoe. The last episode in the series will have screened. You'll be happy.

Six months later, during a spell of summer heat, your father will die. Life as you know it will go to pieces. Over time, mould will appear where you and your mother forget to clean because, with him gone and you eating less and less, there will be other things to worry about. It's the weakness of him, the faint red, still there, still flickering, somewhere, somehow, still in the boat. The loss of him will wax and wane in ways you can't fathom as yet, nearly erase you, make you run when there's no need, look at life like an ashtray to be emptied, not once with the intention to kill you, but never quite telling you this the way your father might have done.

[Home is a heart.]

Home is a heart,   is spring silverfish, spring
cockroach.   Home thicks in the middle.
Home could use some attention.   Home is broken
can openers (three),   is doors that don't hang
square in the frames—open up or down
instead of out, or not at all.   Home eats a salad
                            with too much dressing.
Home loses a job and writes poems,
smacks, waxes, crumbles, peels, like bathtub skin—
huge watery blister.   Home is someone in the kitchen
frying eggs in butter.   Home is a millstone,
is space rock floating behind the moon.
        Home's a pile of sugar so high you can sled down it,
it blows up   because there's a meth lab inside.
Home collects orange peels
                    behind the trashcan by the nightstand,
itches between the shoulder blades until I scratch it.
                    Home is good at fucking.
Home is a bone   warmer, is an open
                            envelope with the wrong name on it.
Home can't remember the last time home felt like themself.
        Home opens—not yet, but they do.   Home quiets
like the A at a certain time of day, once children
                            are gone and it's just everyone else,
too tired to make noise or hear noise. Home is an oil slick
        in the shape of my father,   is a match
held over my father's head.   Home churched,

had beams of singing and sits in a strip mall.
Home is white, is fragile, needs to be torn down.
                    Home is something, maybe.
Home nestles like small mammals.   Home hasn't cried
about not being themself lately, has too much to do.
      Home owes somebody.   Home is a faggot.
Home is queer as fuck.
Home wears dresses without shaving their beard.
                    Home is a Russian salmon pie
we make again with more cream this time,
is an exact number of cards. Home can see the future,
can be seen through the future like an old movie
they're remaking poorly.   Home isn't drunk, but wants
      to be.   Home is a typeface
you can't name in a book you love,
is a shitty poem.   You like
              home for no reason you can figure.
Home is part of speech,   can be spoken
again, again, opening like gills like water like hook.

Trevor Ketner

The Space Between Bottles

Oliver Keogh

'Shouldn't be much longer,' Una calls from the bathroom.

Stan turns from the window and watches her reflection. The bathroom mirror is fogged except for a cloud of clarity Una has cleared with the hair drier. She leans in and daubs her philtrum with a tanned circular pad. She notices him watching, pauses mid-daub and smiles. He acknowledges her with a widening of his eyes then returns his gaze to the street below.

It is just getting dark and an imperceptible rain falls on the commuters as they hurry, sheltered by their umbrellas, towards the end of their day. A cat slinks under the hedge along the footpath, its fur weighed down by the rain.

'Not sure it's the best time of year to come here,' Stan says without turning.

'We can hardly change the time of year we met, can we?'

Una stands in her underwear in the doorway with the sponge pad in her hand.

Still laying the foundation.

'Can you crack on there? It takes you long enough without the insertion of breaks.'

'I'm pausing, not breaking.'

She's happy. Encouraging badinage.

'Look,' he says to her faint silhouette in the window, 'I've come across many of your like before: you take the liberty of a pause, then it becomes an established break, and the next thing, you're unionising on me and demanding it as a right. So kindly hop back in there, and don't come out without the finished product.'

Una scoffs. 'Huh! You're not on one of your building sites now.'

'I'm all too aware of that,' Stan says, eyeing her silhouette. 'Health and Safety would never let you away with that rigout.' He smiles but she does not move. 'Hop along then.'

'I will once you've answered me.'

'Answer you what?'

'Do you want to change the date of our anniversary?'

'No.' He drops his eyes to the canopy of umbrellas. 'We'll leave things just as is.'

Anniversary? Can it even be called that? More an approximation of our first hookup. If it wasn't for the work calendars we'd have no idea. Both too drunk to know. Nine years. What's that? Neither here nor there. Not quite the double digits—nice round ten. Nine. Odd but not prime. Three times three: a trinity of trinities. Suppose there's something to that. Holy J'sus mother of god and the Blessed Saint Joseph. That's three but not the trinity you idjit—wrong daddy. Father son holy spirit. Ah that's the lads.

Stan turns from the window, sits slowly into a beige lounge chair and eases back into its folds. A faint discontinuous hum is coming from the bathroom; it is familiar yet strange, and reminds him of his mother, but he cannot think why. He scans the room. The disturbed coverlet and two flattened pillows mock his earlier endeavors, looking like someone lay back to flick through a magazine.

The suite of suitcases Una bought six or seven years back lay open in descending order, along the far wall. In the front room of their flat in Willesden Road, Stan had asked why three as she displayed their telescopic handles and extendible sides, and Una just smiled and pointed out a hidden pouch. They took to calling them the three bears but that had faded and stopped. They never discussed who was to blame.

The hubbub from the street below gets louder and Stan's temples contract. He stands, puts his wallet in his right pocket, his mobile in his left, and white plastic keycard in his back right trouser pocket.

'I'll be downstairs when you're ready,' he says towards the bathroom.

'I'm just about done.'

'You were about done ten minutes ago. I'll see you downstairs.'

He leaves, the metal door closer pulling the door tightly shut.

*

'Same again, please,' Stan says in an undertone, his face flushed at having to use English. The barmaid acknowledges with a reassuring smile and reaches for the dispenser. Her tired white blouse is messily tucked into a shiny black skirt. Stan shifts his gaze to the clear liquid as it tumbles into the glass and breaks on the ice. He notices the clock above the bottle, and in a swift movement pulls back the sleeve of his left arm.

The barmaid places the glass in front of Stan and removes the empty. She gently lifts the brown water jug and, satisfied with its weight, returns to her magazine at the end of the bar. Stan looks out to the street but the glare of the sun on the window makes him turn away. He rubs his right eye with the heel of his hand.

Best make this the last. Get to that gallery or she'll twig something. Have to have been somewhere. Certainly can't be here.

Last night. What a complete disaster. Hit it too hard. Why though? Why last night above all nights? Why not just celebrate the anniversary like a normal person? No reason. Never seems to be. Just full throttle no excuse whatsoever. Some head on her this morning. Couldn't drag you out of the bar… Table gone by the time we get to the restaurant… Almost had a row with your man. What'd you call him? Maître d', that's it. Hardly his fault. Wander the square. Whole place crowded. Settle for a cubbyhole tucked in a corner. Comment on its quaintness, good Lord, the eyes staring across, like Superman's ready to laser me in two. Zzzeeet, off with me sallynoggin. Nothing for it only to order a bottle or red. Another glare. The menu not even opened. She has to start with prawns and a *small* glass of house white. Couple of attempts at conversation, all shot down. Have it your way. Don't blame me if I'm blowing the head off of you later. Sure enough, mouth going a mile a minute. No shutting meself up. Only remember ordering a third bottle but not finishing it.

Stan toys with the glass, twisting it in circles with his thumb and forefinger. He watches the remains of the milky white liquid swirl and lap, empties it with a protracted swig and sets it on the countertop with a twirl. Looking up, reflected in the blotchy-faded bar mirror, between the Pernod and the Belvedere, a young woman is seated at a round marble-topped table.

The barmaid looks up from the magazine and moves to take her order, Stan raises his glass and nods for another. With head fixed forward but eyes aslant, he watches the space between the bottles.

What brings you here on such a fine day? Sneaking a quick few, huh? Can hardly blame you. Aren't we in the same boat. No good me throwing stones. Or glasses, ice cubes or whatever… Local, definitely local. Got that continental look. Sophisticated. Blonde hair. No, brown. Both. Brown by the roots. Well holy god, not happy with herself. What chance have I eh? Just trendy, I suppose. Or indecisive? Why have one when you can have both. A bottle of red and a bottle of white… Ah, of course. Coffee. What else would you be having at this hour. Maybe you'll lace it with whiskey once your one turns her back… No, no chance of that. You can hardly say you have her ticket now, can you? Been a while since you could say that of anyone. Sharp once. Gone a bit blunt… What do we have here? What does that say? Are you kidding yourself. You'd want to be looking over her shoulder to read that. Second-hand though. Classy. Recycled pleasure. Woman in a cafe reading. Hair coiled behind one ear. Few stray wisps catching the light. Thumb resting on the lower lip. Other hand on the book. Lost in fiction. Skin the colour of buttermilk. Flawless except for that solitary freckle. Just off-center to focus attention. The detail that completes the picture. Turner's red buoy.

Stan's left leg vibrates and his stomach flexes. He retrieves the phone from his trouser pocket. A text message from Una: *Finished. See you at the museum?* He quickly types: *I've left already. Lets meet in the main square and we'll grab a bite to eat.* He looks to the end of the bar and clears his throat loudly. The barmaid looks up, he scribbles in the air and goes to the toilet. When he returns he deposits thirty euro on the counter next to the white slip, slides it towards the barmaid and nods his thanks. He is concerned that the six euro gratuity is too much but doesn't have the time nor the stomach for the exchange. He leaves without a look towards the marble-topped table where the woman is seated, and turns right for the gallery.

There has been a light shower while he has been indoors. The smooth cobblestones shine, and Stan nearly loses his footing twice. In the forecourt of Saint Gatianus' two men are settling on a bench, placing their bags beneath. Stan crosses diagonally in front of the cathedral without blessing himself and continues down the road, skips up five steps to the Musée des Beaux-Arts and enters. A family of three is buying tickets at the kiosk; Stan passes them and goes to the shelves lined with postcards. He scans them slowly, turns and leaves.

The restaurant is busier than the night before. Stan looks for the maître d', and is happy he's not there. Two tables are joined at the back of the restaurant, and a mixed group of eight revel in animated conversation. Una is seated at a small table for two looking out on the square.

'Sorry, I'm late,' Stan says taking a seat. 'Here long?' He tears a piece of bread and chews away the smell of the pastis.

'Not too long,' Una says, distracted. 'How was the museum?'

'Not great, to be honest. Quite a selection of fourteenth and fifteenth century religious art, but not really my thing. They'd a couple of Impressionists; nothing to write home about, really.' Stan looks for the waiter. There are two attending to the group. 'How 'bout you? What'd you get up to?'

'Nothing much. I'd a bit of a strange morning.'

Stan's left hand is raised. He wants to click his fingers. 'How do you mean?'

'I was at the shops, and after a while I realised I couldn't remember what shops I'd been in or what I'd looked at, so I decided to wander down to the river. Then I came across two cats. One was cornering the other, arching its back with its tail erect, the other was cowering, its tail furled. It was terrified. I was terrified. Next thing, the big one chased the other down a stairwell, and the squeaks and squalls that came out of there—I tell you—was unnatural. I stood frozen. Then all of a sudden, it stops, dead. I mean there was nothing. I wanted to know what happened; to see if the poor thing had been killed or what, so I head down slowly but at the bottom, there was nothing.'

Una stops. Stan is looking for the waiter.

'Okay? Where'd they go?'

'Is this boring you?

'Not at all. So?'

'There was a railing. They either got through the bars or under it.'

Stan sighs and looks for the waiter. There is one behind the bar. He raises his hand, 'Excuse me!'

'But the thing was,' Una continues, 'I walked to the river but I couldn't get it out of my mind. I mean, why didn't the cat slip through the bars before? Why did it stay there and just take it?'

Una looks at Stan. He shrugs his shoulders. 'How do you expect me to know? Maybe it had a gammy leg or something,' he offers and turns to order a bottle of Chinon.

'Gammy brain, more like,' Una snaps. 'Anyway, it made me think of us.'

'Sorry?' Stan leans forward with feigned surprise. 'One cat tearing the shit out of another reminded you of us? This is going to take some unpacking.'

He sits back in his chair and smiles. The waiter brings the wine. Stan waves off the tasting and aligns the cutlery until he finishes pouring. Stan narrows his eyes.

'What exactly did it make you think?'

'Just about us.'

There is silence. A piece of cutlery hitting the floor rings from the kitchen.

'Anything in particular?'

'Oh, give it a miss,' she snaps. 'What would you think I was thinking of?' Stan shrugs. Una takes her glass and rests back into her chair. 'I'll be forty in seven months, Stan… And the two of us, the two of us are just doing loops. I think maybe…' She pauses and then blurts, 'I think it's time to call it quits.'

She looks at his face but not his eyes. She holds her glass with both hands—left hand supporting the base, the stem between thumb and index finger, like a priest holding a chalice before the offering.

Stan looks around the restaurant than pulls his chair into the table. He slides the glass of wine to the right, unites the fork with the knife and sweeps them towards the wine. He places his elbows on the table, crosses his arms and leans forward, 'That's hardly the solution, is it?'

'I know it isn't, but it's something. It's movement at least.'

Una waits for him to respond but he remains silent with his eyes fixed on the edge of the table. She exhales and her lips quiver. Una then takes a long slow drink and Stan relaxes.

*

Stan sits in the armchair swirling a glass on the right armrest. The curtains are drawn, the street below blocked from view. He looks at Una's half-lit face as she sleeps. Her lipstick is smudged and mixed with Chinon stain on her upper lip.

She'll be annoyed when she wakes. Make-up all over the place. It will all turn on what happens in the morning. She'll either hit the drink or go dry. Approaching forty. Big step. Nice and symmetrical. Thirty-nine now though… odd but not prime. Three thirteens. Huh. What do you get when you multiply luck by misfortune? Which one wins? Three times luckier or are you thirteen times as misfortunate? That three keeps popping up. Three times one. One times three. One plus two. Or the other way around. One plus one plus one. One's a frightfully useless number. Nothing to it. Weak. Minus one. There's a powerful number. Multiplying that by anything is a completely different kettle of fish.

Stan toes off his shoes, stands, unbuttons his shirt and throws it over the arm of the chair. He undoes his trousers and they drop to the floor. He sits on the edge of the bed, pulls them off and flings them onto a chair. He switches off the lamp and gets into bed. In the dark his hand reaches until it finds Una. He rests the back of his hand against the base of her spine and closes his eyes.

Hope she joins me for a drink tomorrow.

nth

You want to know how to tell the difference between the snake that is harmless and
the snake that will kill you, and the answer is you can't. *Red and black safe for Jack,*

red and yellow et cetera, but you won't remember this when it's zigzagging through
the grass for you like lightning, so all you can say is *oh, I guess this is happening then.*

And you'd think I'd just avoid the woods, but I never do, the truth is this isn't about
snakes at all, but you don't even know, do you? That I've met you before, in other

bodies with different names, all just as kind and disappointing, I should have
known better but it's just that this one kept smiling at me, this one,

you. Coral, or king. Kept touching my arm somewhere that wasn't the wrist, my back
somewhere that isn't the small; vague parts of me that don't have names, so you could

mean nothing. Go ahead, guard your king while I paint my mouth coral, go call a
poem
beautiful and laugh at everything else; go catch your train into another life, stop

on the staircase and look back at me. Ask *what's up,* but don't ask what's wrong,
there's
an answer to that you don't want to hear, now what I want to hear is *it's his loss and I*

hope he chokes on it, his loss, yours. But really it's all mine, isn't it? The heart wants
what it et ceteras, the heart draws the venom towards itself, the heart spares the rod

and lets the snake grow fat, but I've had my whole life to get good at getting over it.
This whole life. So if you've perfected saying thanks but no thanks, and I've perfected

feeling nothing after everything, let's do that without ever speaking; if we can't be
perfect together we can at least be perfect at the same time. So hey guess what,

guess what, guess what, it's safe for Jack again, this is all already
ancient history, my man—but if this is all I'm ever going to get,

then by god I'm going to keep on getting it, I'll take it
wherever I can find it, in the shared kitchens of

the houses I move into, in the crowds across the street just before
the light goes green, each time like it's the only

time that matters—on the bridge spanning the cold width
of the river, in the gutter with the stray wrappers,

stray footprints in the mud, stray birds in the grass, where I pick it up
and dust it off and unhinge my jaw and swallow it, whole.

Stefani Tran

Redesdale Estate, 1956

For Caitriona Crowe

First, this old clock. As I dismantle it,
A child of indeterminate age
On the garage floor, the cogs and flywheels
Buzz, the hour-hands race and stop,
Go back on themselves,
And I peer, like a little god,
In the workings of time. Steady,
The ticking starts, suburban days
Falling into place
Like memory. Glass front doors
And front room windows
Are black depths, to be looked into
Afterwards, when the time is right.
But for now, each pebbledashed house
Is a Freudian box of tricks,
Pre-conscious, locked in itself,
Respectable, safe, like Nineteen Fifty Six.

Pounds and ounces, pennyweights and grams—
A grocer's measuring instruments
Sift reality, slicing ham
And butter, trowelling sugar in brown paper bags
For all of us blow-ins, on whom the hag
Has roosted, the hag of Ireland,
Stateless... Lord Redesdale,
Whoever you were, you gave us the myth of a State,
You left us your name
To conjure with, on your sold estate,
And fled to England, clutching the deeds.
DeValera set us down here, and bade us breed.

A new generation. A clean slate
For history to write on. Non-attachment
Our middle name. Sleepless, we hear
The cattle-drive, to the milking-sheds
Of Stillorgin, in the early hours,
Like the lost morning of a mythic race
Our fathers snore through. De Valera,
Give us our pasteurised milk, and cleanse our blood
Of impurities. Banish the gypsy horses,
Their mounds of fertile dung,
From our gardens. Tinsmiths' fires
Will burn themselves out, the caravan train move on—
Give us leave to live here…

O the pain

That first winter of consciousness—
Snowballs, tainted with copper sulphate,
Crash against my ears. The Zen command
To awaken! Child, it is too late
To run in tears to Mother.
She points to the orphans, filing through the estate
From nowhere to nowhere, shadowed by Sisters
Terrible in their winged headgear
Out through the age of innocence, into the years
Undreamt by De Valera, Connolly, Pearse.

Harry Clifton

The Accursed Questions

1

The girl behind the bar is in love with you, do you know that?
Look at what happened to Kierkegaard, Dostoyevsky—
Sad lives, early deaths, the world no better a place.

It is cold in the kitchen, but you feel nothing,
Reading... The Russians, too, never felt their own weather
In all those fictions. It came from inside them.

People out walking, on the East Pier,
Swarm in their thousands, ghosts of the Nevsky Prospekt.
Where do they come from? Where on earth do they vanish to?

2

Grey-haired now, the girl behind the bar
Has given up on children... And for forty years
No-one has disturbed it, the white cold silence of the kitchen.

The bollards are still grass-grown, on that other pier
Across the water, where time stops
And a decommissioned lightship rusts at anchor.

Half the world has gone to its death. But you,
You are still eighteen, the ice on the Neva
Still unbroken, life unreal outside the hermitage wall.

Harry Clifton

The Follies

Erica X Eisen

A visitor to the Dromana Estate would not be faulted if their first feeling upon arrival was confusion: the gatehouse that greets them from the road is no straightforward structure but a bizarre mélange of far-flung architectural vocabularies. The stonework, the wrought-iron quatrefoils, the pointed windows with their delicate tracery—all of this recalls the cathedrals of the High Gothic. But the bulbous onion dome and spindly minaret-like towers at each of the building's corners, on the other hand, seem to spring straight from Mughal design. Yet we are in neither the France of Abbot Suger's Saint-Denis nor the India of Agra Fort; we are at Villierstown in Waterford, where Henry Villiers-Stuart, a Tory MP and the county's Lord Lieutenant, had the strange structure made to fete his return from his honeymoon. Like a sphinx, half-woman, half-beast, the gatehouse arrests those walking by with the riddle its hybrid body poses to all who pass.

*

In architecture, a folly is a structure whose primary purpose is aesthetic titillation. The Roman artilleryman-turned-architect Vitruvius canonised three virtues that every good building should strive for: *firmitas*, *venustas*, and *utilitas*, or solidity, beauty, and utility. Follies cast off the latter, pitching into the world off-kilter like a lame horse; their designers are the brick-and-mortar equivalents of the tercento monks who, bleary-eyed from copywork by candlelight, fill the margins of their vellum pages with fantastical chimeras or exotic creatures never seen within the borders of their homeland. Grecian temples are grafted onto the rolling hills of Devon; a Habsburg pleasure palace may play unlikely host to a faux pagoda.

In an article for *The New York Times* in 1988, the British travel writer Eric Newby claims, 'It is safe to say that Britain and Ireland contain what must be the known world's greatest assemblage of follies.' Such buildings are not without their enthusiasts: the Irish Georgian Society, whose logo is an image of Conolly's Folly in Co. Kildare, offers books, lectures, and picnic tours of the country's follies and raises funds for their continued preservation. Yet there is something queer at follies' core, a void papered over by forms fantastic. Shorn of place and purpose, follies are undiluted semblance. They are what comes from mixing money with cement.

*

To see a ghost estate is a disturbing experience: block after block of homes unfinished, uninhabited, like a stage set for suburbia awaiting actors. With no one to care for them, lawns are overgrown and left to die; rotted fence posts slump over as though with fatigue; walls still unsided are as grey as the sea before tempest. Without occupants to fill these houses, to furnish them, to brighten them up, blank windows stare out like the empty sockets of a sun-bleached skull. Neighborhoods that never were, these estates are the Irish landscape's most enduring scar from the Great Recession.

As Ireland's economy returns from its post-2008 bottoming-out point, the most recent report by the Department of Housing states that the number of ghost estates has gone down sharply from the three thousand that once existed. Yet by the government's own admission the remaining hundreds of estates, which comprise thousands of empty homes, represent the hardest rehab cases. Like the ornamental hermit's grottoes that peppered the most fashionable of eighteenth-century gardens, these houses stand like strange and not-quite-believable imitations of life. If follies are at bottom imitations, then ghost estates are follies that ape not Roman temples or Norman abbeys but kingly American sprawl, large and languorous. Devoid of an active present, evacuated of the animating warmth of inhabitation, they are semblance incarnate. They seem and seem and seem; they are surfaces that yield not to depth but only to more surface, again and again and onwards to infinity.

*

At the time of his death in 1729, William 'Speaker' Conolly, the son of a Donegal innkeeper, was by some estimates the richest man in Ireland; despite his Catholic background, Conolly nevertheless managed to stake out a place for himself among a Dublin ruling class that was both Anglo and Anglican. He earned his nickname by ascending to the dominion's highest seat of power, doing so at a time when the Irish House of Commons over which he would preside was busy drafting a series of Penal Laws meant to drastically curtail the civil liberties of Catholics. When Conolly died, he left his wife, Katherine, a sizable country estate and a large sum of money with which to modify it as she saw fit for the remaining decades of her mortal life.

Perhaps the peak of Mrs Conolly's architectural ambitions was reached with the Wonderful Barn, a structure which Newby calls 'almost impossible to describe coherently.' The folly's central conical tower, bulbous and blindingly white, juts out incongruously from the centre of an otherwise unremarkable grey farm building. Its sides are speckled with triangular and circular windows; its top is crowned with battlements that give it the appearance of an outsized chess rook. If the Wonderful Barn takes architectural cues from anywhere, it is from Brueghel's fevered vision of the Tower of Babel: massive, weighty, corkscrewing upward towards the sky, towards the dove-coloured clouds, towards some unbounded and inchoate desire for height.

Like other members of the genteel class who commissioned follies on their Irish estates, Mrs Conolly did so as an act of famine relief, employing local labourers to build shell castles, obelisks, and other strange constructions after the famine of 1740-41 caused disastrous crop failures nationwide. Acts like these, which seem at first blush to be measures of freely given kindness, were a product of the reigning ideas of liberal *laissez-faire* economics at the time, which held charity to be not merely economically ill-advised but morally corrosive, inducing idleness in those who received it. In view of this, then, construction programmes like the Wonder Barn extracted needless toil out of starving people their overseers were unwilling to simply feed.

George Orwell makes similar observations in *Down and Out in Paris and London*, his autobiographical account of poverty and homelessness. Orwell's time in shelters and flea-infested tenements led him to challenge what he calls society's 'fetish of manual work': 'It is taken for granted,' he writes, 'that a beggar does not "earn" his living, as a bricklayer or a literary critic "earns" his.' The proliferation of useless or mostly useless work in modern society—and the insistence that members of the working class derive their social value from employment—is rooted in nothing more, Orwell contends, than 'fear of the mob. The mob (the thought runs) are such low animals that they would be dangerous if they had leisure; it is safer to keep them too busy to think.' Such logic seems also to undergird the famine-relief follies that dot Ireland's landscape: at bottom, such projects are exercises in the upper-class revulsion at the idea both at the idea of giving aid for aid's sake and—heaven forfend—the enactment of larger systemic changes that would render such aid unnecessary.

*

In a press conference following the August 2016 EU regulatory decision that Apple owed billions of dollars in back taxes, Competition Commissioner Margrethe Vestager stated that the company's 'so-called head office only existed on paper. It has no employees. It has no premises, and it has no real activities.' Through the creation of 'ghost companies,' the corporation reaped the benefit of Ireland's tax haven status; shiftings its intangible property to Ireland also netted Apple major gains and seemed to supercharge the country's GDP without in any way influencing the lived experience of the economy on the part of Irish citizens, an effect described by Paul Krugman as 'leprechaun economics'. This, too, is another way of seeming, another kind of glass-domed falsity constructed in the gardens of the wealthy.

*

Between 1845 and 1852, the Great Famine dealt the population of Ireland a blow from which it still has not recovered. Killing a million and forcing another million abroad, it sowed a pernicious spirit of emigration that remains deeply rooted within the cultural psyche even today. The current population of Ireland is just short of 4.8 million; the 1841 census conducted by the British counted over eight million souls.

The spate of building projects (both public and private) created in wan-faced response to the Great Famine must be understood in contrast to their mirror: mass tenancy clearances that led to the eviction of hundreds of thousands of subsistence farmers. Most forced clearances came on the orders of landlords eager to amalgamate unprofitable smallholdings into larger, more lucrative tracts and to avoid financial responsibility for destitute tenants. Estimates of the number of Irish peasants subjected to forced eviction, which run to half a million, do not include those farmers who gave up their land 'voluntarily' in order to qualify for famine relief under the increasingly draconian Poor Laws, which barred admittance into workhouses to anyone with a quarter acre or more. As the surest way to prevent the evicted from squatting on their land was to level any buildings there, some landlords went so far as to induce former tenants to raze their own homes by offering them a small sum in payment. The golden age of folly architecture in Ireland therefore took place against a countervailing wind of unprecedented residential destruction borne by the very class of people who were employed in the building of fantastically useless ruins.

*

In the wake of the Grenfell Tower fire that claimed eighty lives largely due to the cheap, flammable cladding used on the housing block's exterior, civil planners on the other side of the Irish Sea have faced a reckoning: decades after the start of the pre-crash construction boom, major questions are being raised about the structural soundness of the era's building projects. In an article for *Engineers Journal* published after the disaster last year, chartered engineer John Brennan cited Ireland's 'regulatory system ... based on self-certification by owners, designers and builders' as leading to dangerous vulnerability in the country's Celtic Tiger housing; asked whether an incident as deadly as Grenfell Tower could happen in Ireland, he concludes, 'Unfortunately, the answer is yes'. An *Irish Times* piece detailing the 'appalling' state of the country's construction standards gives the example of a flat whose toilets were not connected to the pipes but simply dumped excrement beneath the floor. Are these not follies too, after a fashion: sham houses like sham ruins, counterfeit buildings and Potemkin towns, dwellings built with no thought for the form or substance of the lives led inside them?

*

Of the type of folly known as the *ferme ornée*, the most complete example today is Larchill in the north of Kildare. There, what greets visitors is less a farm per se than an Arcadian idyll: acres of splendid countryside in which you will find a dairy in the form of a loggia; a faux-medieval tower encrusted with cockle-shells carefully arranged by the lady of the manor; a mock-Gibraltar whose miniature battlements once looked over naval battles reenacted on the property's lake; and the Fox's Earth, a refuge for foxes built after the owner began to rue his own zealous hunting habits.

There is a tension at the heart of the concept of a *ferme ornée*: the need to hide a farm's less charming aspects for the sake of fostering fantasy, the desire for the picturesque and lovely that erodes the estate's ability to function. Ostensibly bucolic snapshots of a vanished world, the *ferme ornée* instead presents as natural a great deal which is strange: the architecture, with its impossible mash-up of places and times; the menagerie, which frequently brought together exotic strains from far-flung corners of the earth; and the social order upon which estate life is based, which is no natural thing at all. In their honeyed view of farm life, *fermes ornées* presented an image of agrarian existence devoid of agrarian poverty, agrarian hardship. That virtually all *fermes ornées* have fallen into ruin is a testament to the fundamental instability of the illusions upon which they are built.

*

If streets and skylines may readily reveal the grandeur of the past in stately façades or the optimism of the present in the glistening metallic swoops and whorls of starchitects, they also yield up—if one is prepared to look more closely—more knotted notions of civic history. Like gold threads glinting from a woollen tapestry, the gleam of monuments and megastructures overlies the warp and weft of broader life into which attitudes about society—and especially the relative positions of the poor and the wealthy—are inextricably woven, legible often in the space between ostentation and actuality.

Where once stood Nelson's Pillar now stands the Spire: a needle of stainless steel that juts almost four hundred feet into the sky, the world's tallest sculpture. Built in 2003 at the foot of the GPO, the Spire is verticality and nothing else. Its stylistic blankness carries no dialogue with the city around it, not with the stately Georgian buildings and not with the gaudily colorful shops that line O'Connell Street; today, the structure seems like nothing more than an obelisk commemorating the monetary frippery of the pre-bust Celtic Tiger, an impression not helped by the occasional news stories about the expense of the structure's maintenance, such as a February 2015 report in *The Journal* that a replacement bulb for the Spire's crowning light—predicted to cost €10,000—had not been foreseen in the planning stage of the Spire's construction. What does it say about Dublin that such a structure is at its heart? The official name of the Spire, which I have never heard used, is the Monument of Light. As to who the monument is for or what the light should be illuminating and for what purpose, however, there is no plaque to guide us.

Overnight

Saba Sams

Maxine saw him first through the viewfinder of her Snapchat. His face was far-off, turned in the opposite direction to the rest of the crowd, so the strobes picked him out like a full moon. She zoomed in, pulled him into focus, watched for a while. His hair was longer. He'd shaved three slits into his left eyebrow. He was turned to talk to a girl, tall, dancing slightly behind him. They were sharing a Red Stripe.

Maxine put her phone in her bra and shouldered her way outside. The sky was all foamy blues and pinks. Sunrise had come around fast. She found a corner of the smoking area to roll a cigarette, her ears ringing out into the cold.

His name was George. Maxine had met him in Primark, the last day of summer before the first day of secondary school. Their mums had got chatting while shopping for uniforms, last minute and on the cheap.

school shop sixteen pound a polo

the cheeky bastard fuckers

So they'd stood side by side in silence, their eyes on the floor, as trousers were held up to their narrow hips, shirt sleeves pulled tight along the lengths of their arms. Maxine could hear George's iPod Shuffle, very faint, left going in his jacket.

changing rooms jesus have you seen that queue

size up Georgie we're not doing this next year

Afterwards, outside, while their mums smoked cigarettes and laughed like they'd known each other for years, George had pressed one of his headphones into Maxine's palm, and together they'd listened to Sean Kingston's 'Beautiful Girls,' peering out from under their hoods as the low autumn light made stripes on the pavement.

alright love let's get this bus

you'll look out for each other you two won't you

Maxine had only been at the club a few hours. They'd stumbled across it on their way back from a house party shut down by noise complaints. Jos, the friend Maxine had come with, had disappeared a while back. Maxine had assumed that Jos had sloped off home, but she noticed her now through the haze of the smoking area, crouched low and crawling across the black concrete.

Jos

Max hey

you ok down there

yep all good just lost an earring

oh right when

fucking ages no idea

bit shit

yeah

Maxine helped Jos to her feet, waited as she rubbed her palms hard up and down her jeans. The dirt was thick as tar, almost glossy in the new daylight.

you got any wipes or anything

there's sinks inside

you know what Max I'll just have one more look they'll be here somewhere

sure

Maxine dropped her cigarette to the ground and stepped on it. There was nothing for her to do now but go back inside. On the dance floor,

George had turned back to face the DJ. His head bobbed gently to the music, a buoy on a calm sea. Maxine leant against the far wall at the opposite end of the room, next to the door she'd come in by. The crowd had cleared a little while she'd been smoking, so that if George were to turn around he would see her. She stood very still, knowing this, her body reeled in like a kite, waiting.

Maxine was thirteen when her dad moved out. It was then that she'd ended up spending a lot more time with George. Although in school George and Maxine rarely even passed nods in the corridors, their mums had stayed in touch, and long Saturdays spent knocking around each others' bedrooms had made George's flat a familiar second base. The lift up to his floor smelt of piss and he was three bus stops further down the route, but anywhere was better than home in those days, where Maxine's mum shredded up the evenings with her shouting and crying.

stop calling him now please stop

why

he won't pick up you know he won't

it's not that it's the answer machine I like to listen to his voice

mum

let me hear his voice

At George's, Maxine would sit collecting the grime condensed in the grooves of the kitchen table with her fingernail, while George played on his Nintendo DS. At around six, his mum would come home in her leopard coat with polystyrene kebab boxes, and the three of them would sit at the table, eating meat in ribbons and laughing. George didn't have a dad either. After they'd eaten, his mum would pull the cushions off the sofa and make a bed on the floor for Maxine, where she'd sleep in her uniform, a hot water bottle pulled up beneath her sweatshirt. In the middle of the night, she was often woken by George climbing in beside her.

can't sleep again

how come
don't know but it helps sometimes the sound of your breathing

Jos followed Maxine inside after five minutes or so and began working her way around the edges of the room, using the torch on her phone to light up the floor. Maxine didn't move from her place against the wall, where she watched Jos scurry around like an oversized rat, the back of George's head nodding incessantly in the background, slightly faster now to keep in time to the beat.

Maxine thought back to the last place she'd seen George. Two Christmases ago, out of the window of her mum's car. He was walking out a Sainsbury's, something long and white in his mouth that Maxine took for a cigarette, then realised was a lollipop.

was that George back there Max
no no don't think so
you sure looked just like him
positive

The DJ let the last song run out to nothing. The overhead lights were turned on abruptly, so the whole room lit up filthy and stale. Maxine watched as everyone began slowly to file out of the club, except Jos, who hadn't seemed to notice. Some people went to the bar for more drinks but were turned away. The girl that George was with spent a long time untying her jacket from around her waist and pulling it on. George stood waiting, holding her bag out for her to take when she was ready. They were amongst the last people left on the dance floor. Maxine took a step forward, out of the shadow cast by the far wall. George turned finally to face her. He looked up, let his eyes settle on Maxine for a moment, then flick across to the door on her right. Maxine would have questioned if he'd seen her, but she could tell by the way his ears stung red. She let her head swivel, almost of its own accord, so that her eyes could follow George all the way out of the room. He watched the door, unblinking, until he was through it. At one point, he passed so close that she could see the fine, soft hairs on the back of his neck.

Afterwards, when she was sure he had gone, she sunk down into the floor, and sat with her eyes closed, her chin resting on her knees.

It was the summer between year nine and ten, when all the boys smelt of Lynx Africa and Subway. Maxine was a few months from turning fifteen. Her mum had a new boyfriend and a set of boy-girl twins. She seemed very happy and very tired, a map folded back against its creases. Maxine spent most days at home helping; she'd slice cucumbers into sticks that the babies carried off in their mouths to stash behind the couch, where later she'd fish the pieces out again, sogged and linty.

This was also the summer of drinking. George, whose mum stayed out late at weekends, would host small gatherings when the park was rained off. Maxine didn't show at most, but to one she did.

This one. Everyone sitting in a circle with the rain pounding out against the windows. The drink mostly cheap vodka mixed with rip-off Fanta, or that blue WKD. Someone with wine stolen from their parents, finally got open by pushing the cork down into the bottle with the blunt end of a lighter. A box of straights, found in a drawer in the kitchen and shared about the room. Two people being sick by eleven, one in the toilet and the other in the shower. Maxine and George sharing an armchair, his hand moving up and down her thigh.

you never come around any more

stop touching me like that

have another drink

is there vodka still

there is

And then the next morning, suddenly. Maxine woke with a taste in her mouth like an ashtray, George's shapes under the sheets, the sound of a fly dying against the window, a thick bruise across her left hip, and blood, on the tissue after the toilet.

what have you done

what do you mean

His face blank but for a light smirk, his head shaking slowly from side to side, his palms turned upwards in front of him. So she left, walked home through the park, with an image in her head that wouldn't shift: her body as a nut cracked open.

come on girls we're closing up shop

Maxine raised her head to find the club almost completely deserted. She was alone other than Jos, searching through a pile of beer cans in the corner, and the bouncer who was kicking them out.

been a big night has it

no I'm fine

Maxine lifted herself to standing and walked slowly outside, through the smoking area, onto the street and down to the bus stop. Commuters sat lined up neat in their cars. Birds tweeted. Jos caught up, swung her arm around Maxine's shoulders.

sorry I wasn't around much tonight

that's ok

they weren't even pricey

some things are hard to let go of

yeah

On the bus, they sat top deck at the very front so that it felt like they were driving. The sky bloomed huge and blue above them. Maxine picked at the crust of mascara hanging onto her eyelashes and looked out across the park, where thousands of new daisies had sprung up without warning, overnight.

This November, Poetry Ireland in collaboration with The Gallery Press publish *Calling Cards: The Younger Irish Poets*, edited by Peter Fallon and our own Irish-language poetry editor Aifric Mac Aodha. This volume includes selected poems by ten new Irish-language poets with facing translations into English by some of Ireland's finest writers. *The Stinging Fly* celebrates this latest 'comhchealg' with one of these calling cards and its translation.

sliocht as 'Críochfort a Dó'

don fhuinseog scríobh-se is ní don scréachóg

'Dá mbéarfaidís orm,' ar sí,
'Lucht sin custaim agus dlí
ag siúl dom síos an cainéal
contráilte—Ó! Dá mba ghafa mé

le mo mhilliúin punt i nótaí beaga
cuachta istigh im' stoca fada
nó mé faoi ualach cúpla cloch
de chodlaidín mhín a shac an miúil

im' shac go glic i ngan fhios
(agus mé i ndéidh mí a thabhairt
le pobailín dúchasaigh sléibhte
ag teagasc mo chuidse Béarla)—

Cad eile, go deimhin, a dhéanfainn
ach an mianach tá ionam a fhógairt?'

Máirtín Coilféir

from 'Terminal Two'

write for the skylark, not the owl

'If I were to be seized anyhow,' she said, 'seized
by the Customs and Excise
while I was proceeding down the wrong lane,
if I were to be detained

on account of all those millions in small bills
with which my stockings are filled,
or carrying a couple of lumps of opium
the mule just happened to dump

surreptitiously in my rucksack
when I was on my way back
after a month's teaching such English as I've mined
to some little mountain community,

how could I hope to evade
declaring the stuff of which I'm truly made?'

Paul Muldoon

Advice For Those Who Wish To Know The Future

To tell the future
start with a piece of time.
Past, for example, is readily available.
Tear a tiny fraction
for your curio collection. Be careful:
every time you look at it
it changes
—don't trust it.

Find your ancestors' bones
—or, more correctly,
your ancestors' bones will find you.
Work even with the bones
of those you hate.
Making peace with shadows is
why you cast the bones.

Make sure to add the movement
of a planet. It is, after all, the best way
to travel to the future.

Finally, add an eye.
(it only works if it's a fake)

You are now ready to cast your bones.
When you do, pay attention to
the things they don't say.

Keep your ghosts with you. They are what
urges you to ask
what makes you pick up
the bones in the first place.
Ghosts never have answers
—only questions.

Know that the bones
don't have answers either.

Every bone only points at
a lesson that might come. The bones
are great teachers.

When others laugh at you for trying
to know what hasn't happened yet
ignore them. They think that
reading bones is turning inwards
facing away from the future.
They don't understand
it's us who love it most, a love so deep
that poisons us. The bones
are the only antidote.

When those who fear the future come
to seek your counsel
heal them. Tell them
what they already know but are
too afraid to listen.

If you catch yourself wanting to cast them
again and again, remember that
they know as much as you do
that they only speak a language
you're ready to understand.

Be warned: every time you cast the bones
you pay a fee to the universe.
You're robbed of your present
to know the future.
Pay the price wisely.

Be patient.

The future will come
to meet you halfway.

Eleanna Castroianni

Kingfisher

Back home, my eye sockets sprout with birds.
They chirrup electricity and boneless
smoke. We wash the walls in several kinds
of petrol: high octane diesel for me; bricks and
cracked paint of pure unleaded. Something horned

twirls inside my mouth. I lie on my childhood bed
its tendriled spine clacking against mine—
conjoined twins, abalone thorax bones
teeth against teeth, chewing our morning
sisters. Only birdsong can survive

the waste inside us. Where my room is a pill to swallow
the floor is full of tongues. Something oval
breaks inside my mouth. Ossified rage, perhaps,
calciferous shell encasing aviary
amniotics. My tongue sits still at the desert of

a blue feather. On my childhood bed
I give birth to a kingfisher.
Stillborn—
she never draws a single breath. Before I catch her

she's made a nest between my eyes
and all I see

is blue.

Eleanna Castroianni

Winter Hours

Kyle C. Mellen

'You forget,' Beth said to the empty car. 'Everything. Or you think you do. How he smells on the sheets. How your habits are actually his habits. Running a finger around the mouth of a glass right out of the dishwasher. Hating that newswoman's mouth. Listening to Leonard Cohen.' She turned right onto Prentiss Place. No other cars were on the road and Beth hugged close to the steering wheel. Through the windshield the houses looked sturdy and warm. 'Acting like him,' she said. 'Literally acting like him and not even realising it.'

The house was on the right. Beth pulled the car up to the sidewalk before the house and sat looking at it through the passenger window. The house was dark but the lights of the tree were visible through the front window. They seemed to hang there in space. Her brother Peter's station wagon was nosed up to the garage door, covered in a layer of frost.

Jason woke to the swirled white plaster of the ceiling. He stared at it for a moment as his eyes cleared. He thought of cake frosting. The clock said eight-forty. Low, muffled noises like things heard underwater came through the door. He tugged on his penis but without much conviction, then rolled over onto his side and went back to sleep.

*

Cynthia flipped the bacon with a fork and slid the tray back into the oven. From the kitchen table Beth watched the way her sister moved. She was still so lithe. Her movements were like liquid, she poured across a room.

'I'm telling you,' Cynthia said. 'That kid better be up in the next fifteen minutes. Or?' She pointed the bacon fork at the living room. 'OK. I'm sending his sister in there with wet hands.'

'The Christmas spirit,' said Beth.

'Please. Beth?' Cynthia said. 'We were seventeen once. Remember? And we were not allowed to sleep till nine. Nine would've been unheard of.'

In the living room the twins had tired of their toys and lay on their stomachs before the television. Elsie sat between them, taking turns braiding their hair. They were watching some cartoon, something with a cactus that walked and talked. But the sound was off. Grandpa Lon had insisted. On the old hi-fi Bing Crosby was dreaming of a white Christmas. The presents were still wrapped beneath the tree, stockings only until everyone was ready. Peter and Sandy passed a blue mug of coffee back and forth on the couch, each of them reading a paperback. Grandpa Lon sat in his chair looking at the newspaper.

'How's everything going,' Cynthia said to Beth.

'Fine,' Beth said and shrugged. 'It's nice to see everyone all together, isn't it? Dad seems all right.'

Cynthia forked the bacon from the hot pan onto a plate lined with paper towels. She closed the oven and carried the plate to the door. 'We're all troopers,' she said to Beth. Then to the living room: 'Who wants bacon?'

Jason stood naked in the bathroom with the door locked and his hand testing the water of the shower. The bathroom smelled, still, like his grandmother. More than a year and here was Nana as if she'd just left the room. He thought of his dream, of whether he could bring Brittany Grieves into it. Brittany Grieves naked but with boots on. He laughed, it was too ridiculous. And wrong somehow. When the water was steaming up the mirrors he got into the shower.

'I listen to his show sometimes,' Beth told her sister. 'He doesn't sound happy.'

'Please don't do that,' Cynthia said.

'He sounds...' Beth said. She was trying to be as accurate as possible. 'He sounds annoyed. The radio show's his baby and it's like he's not getting any pleasure out of it.'

'Well,' Cynthia said. 'I say good. Serves him right.'

'Cynthia,' Beth said.

'He's a dick,' Cynthia said. She covered her mouth with her hand, grinning.

Beth shook her head. 'He's really not.'

Cynthia took her hand away from her mouth. She crossed her arms and said quietly, 'People heal. They do.'

'I don't know,' Beth said. 'I'm not sure. I have an idea.'

'What?'

Beth picked at a loose thread winding from the placemat. 'I'm still working on it.'

Peter closed his book on his finger and scratched at his beard. It had come to him as a fully formed question. A conundrum. He said it aloud to the room.

'Who delivers the paper on Christmas?' he said. It was for anyone that could answer it, but he looked at Sandy.

Lon lowered the newspaper, bending it in half only by dropping his fingers. Not another inch of him moved. 'What do you mean?' he said. He was frowning.

'Who is it that delivers the paper,' Peter said again. 'Have you ever actually seen anyone delivering it on Christmas?'

Sandy was giving him a look. She set the coffee mug down onto the low table at their feet and closed her book on her finger. 'Honey,' she said, but that was all she said.

Lon said, 'The same person who delivers it every other day. What's wrong with you?'

Peter suddenly wanted to go back to bed. The girls hadn't looked away from the television. The wonder of the question was already gone. Whatever mystery had been there had disappeared.

'Disaster averted,' Cynthia's husband Craig said when he came in the door shaking his shoulders to show everyone how cold it was and holding up the clear plastic bag to show the two quart cartons of eggnog.

'Well thank the lord,' Cynthia said through the kitchen doorway.

On the counter sat a loaf of cranberry bread, their mom's recipe, torn apart and spilling crumbs, the last inch of two-hour-old coffee in the pot, what remained of the plate of bacon, and a stick of butter on its glass tray. Cynthia was pushing half a dozen scrambled eggs around a pan.

'I was going to make eggnog,' Beth said. 'The real stuff.'

Craig entered the kitchen and dropped his coat onto the chair beside Beth. 'Darling sister-in-law,' he said.

They kissed cheeks and Beth said, 'The store stuff tastes like bubblegum.'

'I know,' Craig said. 'I love it.' He set the bag on the counter. The two big boxes of eggnog showed yellow through the plastic. Then he leaned into Cynthia. His hand curled around her waist and he kissed her below the ear.

'Ah-ah,' she said. 'The cook needs her space.' She swatted him away with her free hand and laughed.

Beth watched them and thought a million thoughts that she tried to whittle down to one.

*

Jason came into the living room and waved a hand through the air. His hair was wet and he wore a sweater with a collared shirt under it and blue jeans.

Grandpa Lon said, 'Look who it is.'

'Good morning,' Uncle Peter said. 'Merry Christmas.' Sandy had gone off somewhere.

Jason stood there looking at the room. His cousins, Ava and Renee, were on the floor in front of the old television, the kind that was more like a piece of furniture, wooden and heavy and on the floor. His sister sat between them. The tree lights blinked. He watched his uncle rise from the couch and head down the hall for the bathroom. And Grandpa Lon was back to his paper. Something old was on the stereo, so familiar he hardly heard it. Outside the window the world was mostly brown and no different from other days except that the houses up and down the street had lights in the windows and along the trim. He heard his mom and Beth in the kitchen and he waited an extra moment, longer than was necessary, feeling that he was letting everything build.

His mom stood before the stove. As he entered she looked at him, then at the ceiling, her eyes mock-big, and said, 'At last! I thought we were going to have to drag you out of there.' She reached over to muss his hair. He wriggled away and dug a piece of cranberry bread from the loaf.

He said under his breath but loud enough for them to hear, 'You're the one that let me have whiskey last night.'

'That was your father,' Cynthia corrected.

Jason said, 'You'd think it was Christmas or something.'

'The comedian rises,' Beth said from the table. 'Give me a hug, my hungover nephew.'

'Oh, *Beth*,' Cynthia said. 'Speaking of your father, he's trying to get the old skidoo running, you know.'

'There isn't even any snow,' Jason said.

'There's the rub,' Beth said.

'It is Christmas,' Cynthia said. 'You two haven't heard of miracles?'

The drinks came out at eleven, once the ham was in the oven. Jason was allowed a glass of wine like the adults. Elsie whined. She was twelve, what was the difference?

'Five years?' Cynthia said.

They were all in the living room opening presents. Peter and Sandy gave Lon a new watch. It was sterling silver and waterproof. He could swim down fifty meters without taking it off.

'I can't swim fifty meters down,' said Lon. He held the watch up to the light.

'But you could,' Peter said.

Sandy looked away, scratching a spot behind her ear.

'Thanks,' Lon said. 'It's good looking.'

The twins were racing through the house wielding their toys. Ava held a doll and Renee a trailing blue-green kite that was like a bird. Every so often one of the adults would say, 'No running inside.'

Beth reached under the tree and gathered Jason's present. She held it out to him but then pulled it back. 'Oh shit,' she said. Written across the wrapping paper was 'From Aunt Beth and Uncle Reed.'

'Kids, pardon your aunt's French,' Craig said.

'I forgot to change it,' Beth said. 'I'm sorry, Jason. It's from me.'

'It's cool,' Jason said. He tore through the paper. Inside was the wool blazer that Beth had found in the consignment shop that summer.

'It's from Paris,' she said. 'Never worn.' The pockets hadn't been cut, she explained.

Jason sat cross-legged on the floor. He was nodding, holding the jacket up to show everyone. A nice jacket, charcoal gray, and when he stood to put it on, a good fit. He put his arms out and turned in a circle.

'Beautiful,' Cynthia said.

'Hey, thanks a lot,' he said. He kept it on for the rest of the afternoon.

*

Lon examined the watch Peter and Sandy had given him. And so it was a new watch, one you could go swimming with and not worry about taking off. There was nothing wrong with a new watch. There was nothing wrong with his old watch either.

His family was there, all of them together. It was the one time you could count on it, and it was never as he imagined. But once they left he'd want them back. He knew that. He wanted everyone to stay put for a little longer.

They ate Christmas dinner at precisely three o'clock, just like always. The ham sat steaming on its platter, the table was set. Lon had changed the record to standards by Fiedler and the Pops. The volume was low, just a kind of ambient drone that periodically swelled to claim their attention.

Peter carved the ham and the plates were passed around the table. There was some short and low conversation as they helped themselves to the dishes—mashed potatoes, green beans, carrot soup, a loaf of sourdough bread that Cynthia had made the day before, a big bowl of salad greens, half cobs of corn, Brussels sprouts cooked with onions and garlic and bacon—but once everyone had their food nobody talked. From time to time somebody'd say Good work on the beans or The salt over there? Otherwise the only sounds were plates rocking under knives or silverware tinking off the china.

Then, just like that, everyone leaned back in their seats. They puffed out their cheeks and made their eyes big to each other. Super full, they said. Good dinner. Beth finished her wine and refilled her glass halfway. Cynthia and Sandy were already up and clearing plates. Beth thought about helping but didn't move. Elsie was still eating. She was a slow eater, always had been, and as her mom and Sandy were bringing out the pies and the ice cream, pouring the coffee, Elsie'd only just started on her potatoes. Nobody else seemed to notice.

The most tenuous thing in the world, Beth thought, is a dinner table.

She was the only one remaining when Elsie took her first piece of cherry pie to her plate. From the kitchen came the sound of plates being stacked, the rattle of cutlery, a brief punctuation mark of laughter, the dishwasher rack sliding closed. The family sprawled around the living room like victims, some on the couch, some on the floor, Lon sleeping in his chair, all of them holding their stomachs, their eyes glassy.

'We should just order a pizza next time,' Beth said and was immediately sorry she'd said it. Elsie did not look up. Beth breathed in and on the exhale said under her breath, 'Spirit of light.'

'What's that?' Elsie said.

Beth looked across the table at her. 'It's how my yoga instructor ends a practice,' she said.

Elsie nodded, trying to scoop the cherry filling with her fork. 'Mom does yoga.'

'Yeah?' Beth said.

'She'll be all, like, crying after,' Elsie said.

It was five o'clock and time for the walk. No one needed to say a word. They began pulling on jackets from the hall closet and gathering by the front door. Beth sat in the window seat hugging a knee. Jason was on the floor.

'You coming?' said Cynthia.

Jason flopped a hand and Beth said she was all right too.

Cynthia stepped farther into the living room. 'Take it easy on the eggnog,' she said with her eyebrows raised. 'I know how much bourbon's left.'

'I'll make sure he behaves himself,' said Beth.

'That's very funny, sis. I meant you.'

Beth watched them gather on the sidewalk. The light was falling but not gone and they had that wonderful look of people seen through glass. The girls kicked at something against the curb. Craig pointed up the street, and then the group was moving and breaking apart. Cynthia and Sandy the fastest, Lon and Craig following, the girls off in the street, Elsie alone and staring at the ground, Peter coming up last.

'They're gone,' Beth said.

A light snow began to fall as the party met Lambert Street. The twins called to everyone what was happening. It was snowing. Did they see?

'How about the skidoo now,' Craig said.

'We'll see,' Lon said.

The light was slipping fast. The houses they passed glowed from within, through golden curtains. The beads of strung Christmas lights lent an unreal feeling to the neighborhood. The evening was blue and the snow shook itself across the lawns. Everything was still.

Beth and Jason sat on top of the picnic table in the backyard, their feet on the bench. They hunched forward as the snow began to fall.

'Oh,' Beth said when she noticed. 'Oh.'

Jason kept his smoke in and held the joint toward her. Beth took it between her fingers like a cigarette, watching the sky and what was falling from it. She smoked it like a cigarette too, holding it at the ends of her first two fingers, taking a drag and exhaling.

'It's pretty good,' Jason said.

Below the empty feeder a lone sparrow scratched in the dirt for seed.

'We should fill that,' Beth said.

'Yeah we should,' Jason said. He giggled but choked it back.

Beth said, 'I'm a little fucked up.'

'What kind of bird is that,' Jason said.

Peter watched his girls twirling in the middle of the street and didn't say anything. Sandy and Cynthia were up ahead, their heads down, talking in low voices. His father was behind them. In the street Renee grabbed Ava's sleeve and tilted her head back, her face to the snow, her mouth open and tongue gathering it in. Ava did it too. They all continued walking. Peter was thinking of the long drive home. It was two hours to Auburn and though he was tired the idea of the darkened car was like a gift. Sandy silent, gazing out the window, the twins asleep in the back. There was so much time yet. In the car, Peter knew there'd hardly be a single word spoken once they made the interstate. For two hours it'd be like that, the only noise the hum of the tires over the road, the soft rustling of tired bodies finding the perfect temporary adjustment. And then once they were home and everybody put to bed he would turn on the small lamp on the end table and play a certain Gram Parsons album he had not listened to for years. There was a song already in his head, just a few measures, no lyrics but the notes. He hummed them to himself. Peter closed his eyes and pictured the dark room, the clear notes coming through the headphones, the peace of the oncoming moment.

Jason tapped the roach out against the ground and climbed back onto the picnic table beside Beth. From his pocket he produced a pack of cigarettes. He placed the roach inside and offered her one.

'Oh my god,' she said. 'When did this start?'

'It's just from time to time,' he said.

Lon saw the house appear before them through the blue dark. He didn't want to get there yet. A car drove slowly up the road without headlights.

'Hey,' Lon said and everyone looked.

He was stopped on the sidewalk. Everyone was stopped. The girls stood across the street, reaching to pull cones from a pine tree on the corner of the Verkis lot.

'What's wrong?' Cynthia called back.

He watched the car rising away from them. It slowed at the meeting of Lambert Street and turned left, its lights still off. Lon stamped his feet against the sidewalk.

They began moving again. Lon knew what everyone was thinking, if they were thinking anything. Old Grandpa was getting close to it. The point of no return. He was seventy-nine years old. 'Soon,' Lon said. The family hunched their shoulders against the cold as they met the street.

Jason was telling her about his dream. 'I was driving down this little road. It was in the woods, but I could see the backs of buildings. Like the behind of a strip mall or something. And at the end was this storage building. You know those store-it-yourself places?'

Beth blew her smoke away from him. 'Self-storage,' she said. 'There are always self-storages at the ends of roads like that.' She passed him the cigarette and Jason took a quick drag and held it a little awkwardly, out away from his body.

'I went into it,' he said. 'Inside were hallways full of orange doors. Metal doors. Car doors. No, garage. Garage doors.' He hadn't remembered it but now it was there in his mind as if he were dreaming it again.

'You push them up into the ceiling racks,' Beth said.

'Exactly. The hallway must have been ten miles long. That's what it seemed like. And there were all these other hallways branching off it. Identical ones. Just orange as far as the eye could see.'

'Jeez,' Beth said. She pictured it, how it must have looked. Not just to her but how it must have looked to a seventeen-year-old. For a moment Beth thought she was floating up off the table. She reached out and gripped Jason's elbow, the cold wool of the jacket she'd given him. 'Corrugated,' she said. 'I think that's what you call them. What did you do?'

'I just walked,' Jason said. 'It seemed like days. All those doors that aren't really doors. You know? All that people's stuff in there.'

Beth took the cigarette back from her nephew and looked at it. Jason was staring across the frozen lawn, the empty trees. She placed the cigarette under her foot, against the seat of the picnic table. For a moment she thought of saying something, but didn't. She looked at Jason. Snow was gathering in his hair and on the shoulders of the jacket. It was clear from the way her nephew told it that he knew it was a nice dream.

STINGING FLY PATRONS

Many thanks to:

Hanora Bagnell
Maria Behan
Trish Byrne
Brian Cliff
Edmond Condon
Evelyn Conlon
Simon Costello
Sheila Crowley
Paul Curley
Kris Deffenbacher
Gerry Dukes
Ciara Ferguson
Brendan Hackett
James Hanley
Teresa Harte
Christine Dwyer Hickey
Dennis Houlihan
Nuala Jackson
Geoffrey Keating
Jack Keenan
Jerry Kelleher
Jack Kelleher
Claire Keogh
Conor Kennedy
Joe Lawlor
Irene Rose Ledger
Róisín McDermott
Petra McDonough
Lynn McGrane
Jon McGregor
John McInerney
Finbar McLoughlin
Maggie McLoughlin
Ama, Grace & Fraoch MacSweeney
Mary MacSweeney
Paddy & Moira MacSweeney
Anil Malhotra
Gerry Marmion
Ivan Mulcahy
Michael O'Connor
Patrick O'Donoghue
Kieran O'Shea
Lucy Perrem
Maria Pierce
Peter J. Pitkin
George Preble
Mark Richards
Orna Ross
Fiona Ruff
Alf Scott
Ann Seery
Eileen Sheridan
Arthur Shirran
Alfie & Savannah Stephenson
Marie Claire Sweeney
Olive Towey
Debbi Voisey
Ruth Webster
Grahame Williams
The Blue Nib (Poetry Website)
Hotel Doolin
Lilliput Press
Museum of Literature Ireland
Tramp Press

We'd also like to thank those individuals who have expressed the preference to remain anonymous.

By making an annual contribution of 75 euro, patrons provide us with vital support and encouragement.

BECOME A PATRON ONLINE AT STINGINGFLY.ORG

or send a cheque or postal order to:
The Stinging Fly, PO Box 6016, Dublin 1.

NOTES ON CONTRIBUTORS

Jeffrey Alfier's recent books include *Fugue for a Desert Mountain, Anthem for Pacific Avenue,* and *The Red Stag at Carrbridge: Scotland Poems.* His publication credits include *The Carolina Quarterly, Midwest Quarterly,* and *Poetry Ireland Review*. He is founder and co-editor of Blue Horse Press and *San Pedro River Review.*

Molly Anders is a Kentucky-born writer now living in London, England. She is the recipient of the Joyce Carol Oates Fiction Prize and fellowships from the Norman Mailer Center, the James Merrill House and the J. William Fulbright Commission. She holds a Masters in Fine Arts from Syracuse University.

Clare Archibald is a Scottish writer. 'Parallel of Past Imperfect' is an extract from her hybrid linked sequence of abstractions *The Absolution of Shyness*. She has a photography and words pamphlet forthcoming as part of the Gorse Editions series, will be part of the *Form Ever Follows Function* digital art exhibition in Dublin in 2019, and curates the *Lone Women in Flashes of Wilderness* project.

Katie Burnip is an Anglo Australian fiction writer, based in North London. She is currently working on her first collection of short stories.

Jem Day Calder lives in London. This is his first published work of fiction.

Eleanna Castroianni is a writer, poet and performance storyteller from Greece. Their fiction has appeared in *Clarkesworld, Beneath Ceaseless Skies,* and *Strange Horizons*. Find them at http://eleannacastroianni.wordpress.com or @nomadological on Twitter.

Harry Clifton was Ireland Professor of Poetry 2010-2013. His recent books include *The Holding Centre: Selected Poems 1974-2004, Ireland and its Elsewheres* and *Portobello Sonnets.* A new collection of poems *Herod's Dispensations* is due in Spring 2019 from Wake Forest (US) and Bloodaxe Books (UK).

Máirtín Coilféir was born in Navan, County Meath, in 1986. He holds a BA and PhD from Trinity College, Dublin, and has worked at NUIG and UCD. He is the editor of the academic journal *COMHARTaighde* and is currently working as an assistant professor in the University of Toronto.

Aoife Comey studied English at Trinity College and currently lives in London. 'Employment' is her first published short story.

Kieron Corrigan was born in 1960, a child of the Irish diaspora. He lives in the West of England, and works in NHS mental health services.

Michaële Cutaya is a writer, researcher and editor living in County Galway. She writes essays and reviews for Irish publications in print and online. She co-founded *Fugitive Papers* with James Merrigan in 2011. She is editor at *CIRCA Art Magazine* since 2016.

Erica X Eisen's works have appeared or are forthcoming in *The Threepenny Review,* the *Guardian, Hazlitt, The Paris Review Daily, The Baffler,* and elsewhere. She received her bachelor's degree in History of Art & Architecture from Harvard and her MA from the Courtauld Institute of Art. She is an Irish citizen.

Oisín Fagan has had short fiction published in *The Stinging Fly* and the anthology *Young Irelanders.* In 2016 he won the inaugural Penny Dreadful Novella Prize for *The Hierophants. Hostages,* his first story collection, was published in 2016 by New Island (Ireland) and in 2018 by Head of Zeus (UK). He is represented by C+W.

Nicole Flattery's work has appeared in *The Stinging Fly, The Dublin Review, The White Review,* the *Irish Times, Winter Papers* and on BBC Radio 4. She was the winner of *The White Review* Short Story Prize in 2017. Her debut story collection *Show Them a Good Time* is forthcoming from The Stinging Fly Press (Ireland) and Bloomsbury (UK/US) in 2019.

Sarah Maria Griffin's first novel *Spare and Found Parts* was published by Greenwillow Books (US) in 2016 and Titan Books (UK) in 2018. Her non-fiction has appeared in *Buzzfeed, The Rumpus, Guts* and *Winter Pages*. Her collection of essays about emigration, *Not Lost,* was published by New Island Press in 2013. She tweets at @griffski.

Oliver Keogh was born in County Tipperary in 1975 and currently lives in London.

Trevor Ketner is the author of *Major Arcana: Minneapolis,* winner of the Burnside Review Chapbook Contest judged by Diane Seuss. They have been or will be published in *Best New Poets, New England Review, Ninth Letter, West Branch, Pleiades, Diagram* and elsewhere. They live in Manhattan with their husband.

Kyle C. Mellen's stories appear in *EPOCH, The Georgia Review, The Gettysburg Review,* and *Versal.* A recipient of an Alaska Literary Award and the Sherwood Anderson Fiction Award, he lives in Fairbanks, Alaska.

Paul Muldoon is a Fellow of the Royal Society of Literature, the American Academy of Arts and Sciences and the American Academy of Arts and Letters. In addition to the Pulitzer Prize, he has received an American Academy of Arts and Letters award in literature, the T. S. Eliot Prize and the Seamus Heaney Award for Arts & Letters. He is the recipient of honorary doctorates from ten universities.

Clare Needham is a writer living in New York City. Her work has appeared in *Ploughshares Solos, New York Tyrant Magazine, Burning House Press, Catapult, Bodega Magazine,* and elsewhere. She has an MFA in fiction from Hunter College.

Doireann Ní Ghríofa writes both prose and poetry, in both Irish and English. Among her awards are the Rooney Prize for Irish Literature, a Seamus Heaney Fellowship, and the Ostana Prize (Italy). Her latest book is a bilingual selection of poetry titled *Lies*.

Katarína Novotná is a Slovak woman living in Prague and a former student of Creative Writing in Galway. Her poems remained unpublished until now. She currently works as a translator.

Sean O'Reilly's published work includes *Curfew and Other Stories* and the novels *Love and Sleep, The Swing of Things* and *Watermark. Levitation,* his second collection of stories, was published last year. Sean leads *The Stinging Fly*'s Fiction Workshop. He has served as Writer-in-Residence with Fingal County Council, Dublin City Council and IADT/ Dún Laoghaire Rathdown County Council amongst others. He is a member of Aosdána.

Saba Sams is currently studying an MA in Creative Writing at Birkbeck, University of London. Her short stories have been published online at *Litro, The Forge, The Manchester Review,* and elsewhere. She is a fiction editor at *The Stockholm Review of Literature*.

Stephen Sexton lives in Belfast where he teaches at the Seamus Heaney Centre for Poetry. His poems have appeared in *Granta, Poetry London,* and *Best British Poetry 2015.* His pamphlet, *Oils,* published by The Emma Press in 2014, was the Poetry Book Society's Winter Pamphlet Choice. His first book will be published by Penguin in 2019.

Shriram Sivaramakrishnan is a proud alumnus of Seamus Heaney Centre for Poetry. His poems have recently appeared in *The Fenland Reed, Coast to Coast to Coast, Riggwelter, Pidgeonholes,* among others. His debut pamphlet *Let the Light In* was published by Ghost City P in June 2018. He tweets at @shriiram.

Eloise Stevens is a writer and audio producer, based in London. Her poems have been published by *No Bindings, Jaipur Literature Festival, Helter Skelter, The Bombay Review* and *City of Stories.* Her debut poetry collection, *The Beat of Beast,* was shortlisted for The (Great) Indian Poetry Collective prize and Eyewear's Melita Hume prize. She is currently working on a novel.

Susanne Stich is originally from Nürnberg and lives in the Northwest of Ireland. She was a finalist at the 2018 Irish Novel Fair and just received a bursary award from the Irish Arts Council. Besides *The Stinging Fly* her short stories have appeared in *Ambit, Boyne Berries, The Incubator* and other magazines. She is also a curator and filmmaker.

Sean Tanner's work has appeared in the *Irish Times, The Lonely Crowd* and *The Holly Bough.* In 2017 he received the Hennessy New Irish writing award for first fiction, and in 2018 he received the John McGahern Award.

Stefani Tran is a Vietnamese-Filipino writer, currently in the MPhil in Creative Writing programme at Trinity College Dublin. She's concealed her heart beneath your floorboards, and its ceaseless beating will haunt you. Deal with it. Find her online at stefanitran.weebly.com.

Iain Twiddy grew up in eastern England, and studied literature at university. He has written two critical studies of contemporary poetry.

John Vaughan is a writer from Dublin. He studied English at UCD. He was born in 1996.

Esther Vincent Xueming is co-editor of *Little Things* and teaches Literature at the School of the Arts Singapore. Her poems have been published in *About Place Journal, Split Rock Review, Ghost City Review, Quarterly Literary Review Singapore, New Asian Writing, Eastlit, Into the Void Magazine* and elsewhere. She currently reads for *Frontier Poetry*. Follow her @EstherVincentXM.

Hilary White is from Cork, currently living in Manchester where she works on a PhD on 1960s experimental women's writing, visuality and indiscipline. She is interested in writing fiction which incorporates illustration in various ways. She co-runs a bi-monthly poetry & performance reading series, *No Matter*, in Manchester.

James Wilkes' poetry and prose has recently appeared in *Datableed, The Wire, gorse, The White Review, Minor Literature[s]* and *Poetry Wales.* He is working on a collection of speculative fictions, stories and fragments that respond to the archives of the Peckham Experiment, an interwar health centre in South London.

CORRECTIONS

The following notes on contributors were erroneously omitted from Issue 38. We apologise for the error. Roisin Kiberd's essay 'Bland God: Notes on Mark Zuckerberg' and Serena Lawless' essay 'Kaleidoscope Eye' are available to read in full on our website stingingfly.org.

Roisin Kiberd writes about the internet, culture and internet culture, and has been published by *Vice*, the *Guardian* and others. Despite all her complaints about social media, she can be contacted at @roisinkiberd.

Serena Lawless has an MA in Writing from NUI Galway. She was chosen as one of Words Ireland mentees under their first National Mentoring Programme. Her work has appeared as part of Hennessy New Irish Writing in the *Irish Times*, and she has been awarded a Tyrone Guthrie Residency by Galway City Council. You can find her on Twitter @serenalawless.